CW01020928

JAMES GILES

CHINA AND GLASS PAINTER

(1718-1780)

Helen,
All best wishes
Stephen

Stephen Hanscombe

With a contribution
by
Martin Mortimer

Published in conjunction with
a loan exhibition at
Stockspring Antiques
114 Kensington Church St., London W8 4BH
9th – 21st June 2005

ACKNOWLEDGEMENTS

Stephen Hanscombe, Martin Mortimer, and Antonia Agnew and Felicity Marno of Stockspring Antiques are indebted to the generosity of many people who gave their time and expertise, or lent their objects, to this exhibition. We wish to thank:

Lending Museums:

Ashmolean Museum: The Visitors, Dr Christopher Brown, Timothy Wilson, Dinah Reynolds.
Museum of Worcester Porcelain: The Trustees, Wendy Cook
Holburne Museum of Art: The Trustees , Christopher Woodward, Lisa White,
Bowes Museum: The Trustees, Howard Coutts
Museum of London: The Board of Governors, the Collections Committee, Antonia Charlton.
Gloucester City Museum: Louise Allen

And:
Hilary Young of the Victoria and Albert Museum
Karin Walton of the Bristol Museum and Art Gallery

And also:
Robin Barkla, Patricia Begg, William Buck, Aileen Dawson, Diana Edwards, Helen Espir, Tim Forrest, Harry Frost, Anne George, the late David Howard, John Kirkwood, David Kitson, Hugh Langmead, Ian Lowe, Errol Manners, Anne McNair, Roger Massey, Robyn Robb, John Sandon, Simon Spero, Tom Walford, Mavis Watney, Amina Wright.

The pieces lent by the Ashmolean Museum, Oxford were presented by
Mr and Mrs Henry Rissik Marshall through the National Art Collections Fund
in memory of their only son,
William Somerville Marshall,
killed in action in 1944.

Unless otherwise stated, all pieces are from private collections.

ISBN 0-9550159-0-1

Published by Stockspring Antiques Publications
114 Kensington Church St.,
London W8 4BH
www.antique-porcelain.co.uk

CONTENTS

FOREWORD

It is now more than twenty years since the last exhibition in London of porcelain and glass decorated in the workshop of James Giles. It was held by Albert Amor to coincide with the publication of Gerald Coke's book, *In Search of James Giles,* and was largely made up of items from his magnificent collection, now in the Museum of Worcester Porcelain.

In Search of James Giles is the only book written to date on the life and work of Giles, and all those interested in the subject are greatly indebted to Mr Coke for the research and scholarship that went into its publication. Its first objective was to distinguish between Worcester porcelain decorated in the Giles workshop and that decorated at the Worcester Factory, and most of Coke's attributions have stood the test of time, while some, like the naturalistic birds patterns which were contested at the time, have now been accepted into the Giles canon. The book is also invaluable for the appendices, which bring together most of the documentary evidence relating to Giles - the advertisements, the Christie's 1774 sale catalogue, the list of Giles customers in the ledger, and the checklist of Giles patterns.

Inevitably there are some areas where Coke's conclusions have been overtaken by subsequent research. We now know that Giles was never resident in Worcester, nor was his workshop based in Kentish Town. Coke's views on Giles's relationship with the Worcester Factory have also come under close scrutiny, and one of the purposes of the present exhibition is to bring together, through the catalogue, the results of the recent research that has taken place on the subject.

If Giles opened his workshop as early as 1743, as the evidence now suggests, he was decorating Chinese porcelain for the best part of twenty years. Of the eighty five pieces in the 1983 exhibition only three were on Chinese porcelain, and while the present exhibition has attempted to focus more closely on this area of Giles's work, it still includes only fourteen pieces. There is clearly much more work to be done in identifying the workshop's output on Chinese porcelain, especially from the first decade of its existence.

The Giles workshop produced some of the most beautifully decorated of all Eighteenth Century English porcelain and glass, but Giles's name is scarcely known outside specialist ceramic circles. It would be nice to think that this exhibition might also make a modest contribution to bringing an appreciation of Giles's exceptional talents to a wider audience.

An exhibition of this sort is dependant on help from a range of sources, and those individuals and institutions who have helped on this occasion are listed in the Acknowledgements. I should, however, like to add my own special thanks to Antonia Agnew and Felicity Marno for inviting us to hold the exhibition in their beautiful shop, for designing the catalogue and for arranging the exhibits. Their enthusiasm for the project and their hard work in furthering it have been hugely encouraging. My thanks also to Martin Mortimer who has most generously looked after every aspect of the glass section of the exhibition. Giles porcelain collectors are inclined to overlook the workshop's work on glass, and I am sure all visitors to the exhibition will agree that the inclusion of the glass section greatly increases its interest and scope. I am deeply indebted, too, to David Kitson, Ian Lowe, Simon Spero and to the late David Howard each of whom has read parts of the catalogue and given much helpful comment and advice. They have all been most generous with their time and knowledge.

I would also like to thank my wife, Nicola, who has given me every support and encouragement.

James Giles was born in London in 1718[1], and like many of the finest craftsmen working in England at that time he was of Huguenot stock. His grandfather, Abraham Gilles, originally a silk-worker from Nimes, emigrated to England towards the end of the seventeenth century. Abraham and his son, also James, were naturalized in March 1700. Later their surname was anglicised to 'Gyles', subsequently 'Giles'.

This James, the father of our James Giles, is described as a 'China Painter' in the records of 'The Apprentices bound to the Freemen of the Worshipful Company of Glass Sellers of London' in the Guildhall Library, where the apprenticeship of his elder son, Abraham, is recorded in 1729. Abraham's master was Philip Margas, and his firm, Margas and Co., was a substantial purchaser of Chinese porcelain from the East India Company.

The younger James Giles was apprenticed in 1733. The entry in the Apprentice Books in the Public Record Office reads, 'Monday, May 7th, apprenticed James, son of James Giles of St. Giles in the Fields to John Arthur of St. Martins in the Fields, Jeweller. Indentured from 9th of April 1733, for seven years. Fee, £30, tax 15/-'.

Nothing is known of John Arthur, Giles's master, and it appears that James Giles was his only apprentice. During the eighteenth century apprenticeship to a member of one of the City livery companies was often merely a device for becoming a freeman of the City, and thereby achieving exemption from certain tolls and dues. However, there is no evidence that Arthur was a freeman, and it is likely that Giles's

apprenticeship did involve training of some sort. The word 'jeweller' in 1733 would more probably describe a maker of jewellery rather than a retailer of jewellery, so that assuming that his master was the former, enamelling could have been one of the skills that the young Giles acquired. He would also probably have developed his ability to draw and to work on a small scale.

Giles would have completed his apprenticeship in 1740[2]. The first evidence of his decorating activities does not appear until 1763, when he placed an advertisement in Thomas Mortimer's *The Universal Director* announcing that he was painting 'China and Enamel' from premises in Berwick Street in Soho[3]. It has been generally assumed,[4] however, that before Giles moved to Soho, he had a workshop in Kentish Town, having taken over the premises there of a short-lived china works which ceased trading in 1756. This assumption is based on the testimony of Thomas Craft, who writing in 1790 recalled that 'about the year 1760' he brought a bowl 'in a box to Kentish Town, and had it burnt there in Mr Gyles's kiln, cost me 3/-'. This bowl of Bow porcelain was found in a box in a cupboard in the British Museum in 1851. Craft was one of the Bow Factory's leading decorators, and pasted to the lid was a statement by him, which

[1] Much of the information about Giles's birth, family, and early life was given to Aubrey J. Toppin by a descendant, Henry W. Hall of Eastbourne, and published in *ECC Transactions*, No.1, 1933, *Contributions to the History of Porcelain-Making in London*, pages 31-33.

[2] On 4th July 1745 a James Giles took a lease of a tenement in Worcester. In his book *In Search of James Giles*, page 4, Gerald Coke assumes that this was the same Giles, and that it was when he was living in Worcester that Giles first made contact with the Worcester Factory. However, the Factory did not open until 1751, and Harry Montagu has shown that the Giles named in the lease was a local Worcester man unconnected with our James Giles - see *ECC Transactions*, Vol. 16, Part 3, page 298.
[3] The texts of all of Giles's advertisements are reproduced in Gerald Coke, op. cit. Appendix A.
[4] John Sandon, *The Dictionary of Worcester Porcelain*, Vol. 1, page 177, and Gerald Coke, op cit, page 4.

included a description of the factory, together with the reference to Giles.

The situation was, however, complicated by the existence of a list, published in 1749, of the names of those who voted 'for a Citizen for the City and Liberty of Westminster' between 22nd November and 2nd December 1747'. Among the names is that of 'James Gyles, Berwick Street, Chinaman'. Gerald Coke took the view that this must refer to our James Giles's father,[5] who, as we have already seen, was also named 'James', but, as Hilary Young pointed out,[6] in the known references to James Giles senior he is described as a 'China painter', while it is his son who is referred to as a 'Chinaman', ie a dealer in ceramics and glass, as well as a 'China and Enamel Painter'.

Thanks to the researches of Roger Massey, the position has now been clarified. In a paper entitled *Independent china painters in 18th century London*, read to the English Ceramic Circle on 16th October 2004, he revealed that 'the rate records for the Parish of St James Piccadilly record James Giles in occupation of the same premises in Berwick Street from June 1743 until 1777.' He also reported that he had found the will of James Giles senior, which showed that he had died in 1741. There is, thus, no possibility that the voters' list published in 1749 could refer to Giles senior, and it is, therefore, virtually certain that James Giles junior based himself in Soho in 1743, and that he continued there until he quit the business in 1776/7. The only conflicting evidence remains the testimony of Thomas Craft. The information about the Bow Factory recorded in his statement

is accurate, and it seems out of character that he should have made a mistake about the location of Giles's workshop. However, Craft was writing thirty years after the event, and it is possible that he confused Giles with Robert Chapman, another outside decorator who worked in Kentish Town in the 1760's[7]. The only other possibility is that Giles was using both premises, but this is most unlikely: there is no other contemporary reference to his working in Kentish Town, and there seems to be no reason for his having split his operation in this way.

Assuming that Giles completed his apprenticeship in 1740, he probably then worked in a decorating workshop in order to learn the business[8]. His father was a 'China Painter', but, as we have seen, he died in 1741, so the young James could hardly have trained with him. The contents of Giles senior's will are now known, and a curious feature is that while he refers to his elder son as 'his dear Abram', there is no reference whatever to his son James. There were, however, a number of decorating workshops in London at that time, some owned by fellow Huguenots, and, assuming he set up his own business in 1743, he could have worked at any of them for the three years beforehand. Initially his business was probably quite

---

[5] Gerald Coke, op. cit. page 4, footnote 11, where he also suggests that it was Giles senior's death or retirement which prompted his son's move from Kentish Town to Berwick Street in Soho in 1763 in order to take over his father's premises.

[6] Hilary Young , *Apollo*, Vol. CLVI, no. 490, *Eighteenth-century English decorators of Chinese porcelain*, page 17.

---

[7] Hilary Young, op. cit.

[8] The fact that Giles was described as a 'Chinaman' in the 1747 voters list could mean that when he moved to Soho in 1743 he set up business as a retailer of china rather than as a decorator, and that it was only post 1747 that he started his enamelling business. This is certainly possible, but it seems clear from subsequent references to him as a 'China Painter' and an 'ingenious artist' that he did personally paint porcelain at some stage. In this case he would have been more likely to do his training immediately after he had completed his apprenticeship rather than after he had set up his own retailing business. What seems certain is that he was engaged in retailing long before he opened his Cockspur Street showrooms in 1767.

small, employing besides himself perhaps a couple of apprentices and a journeyman.

Throughout his period of training and the early years of his own workshop his source of undecorated stock was Chinese porcelain, and although none of his work from these earliest days has been positively identified, there is a considerable body of Chinese porcelain dating from the 1750's whose decoration can be attributed to his workshop. Most of these items are from tea and coffee services which are painted with flowers and insects, 'fancy birds', and landscape scenes, and he probably painted some armorial services. Giles also decorated some Bow porcelain around 1760, and it was probably also at the beginning of the 1760's that Giles started to buy undecorated porcelain from the Worcester Factory. Giles's porcelain sources will be examined in more detail in Chapter 3.

The fact that, as has already been mentioned, Giles placed an advertisement in *The Universal Director* in 1763, suggests that that year may have been a turning point of some sort in his career. This publication was owned by Thomas Mortimer, who described it as 'the Nobleman and Gentleman's true Guide to the Masters and Professors of the liberal and polite arts and Sciences, and of the mechanic arts, manufactures,...established in London and Westminster, and their environs'.

Giles's announcement was headed, 'Giles, James, China and Enamel Painter, Berwick Street, Soho'. R J Charleston[9] has pointed out that in the eighteenth century the word 'enamel' could also mean 'opaque-white glass', and that it here refers to the fact that Giles was decorating glass as well as porcelain.

The advertisement went on to state that:

---

[9] R J Charleston, *ECC Transactions,* Vol. 6, Part 3, *A decorator of porcelain and glass - James Giles in a new light,* page 292.

'This ingenious Artist copies the Pattern of any China with the utmost exactness, both with respect to the Design and Colours, either in the European or Chinese taste: he likewise copies any Paintings in Enamel. He has also brought the Enamel Colours to great perfection, and thereby rendered them extremely useful to the curious Artists in that branch.'

No other advertisement by Giles is recorded until four years later, when on 17th December 1767, the first of a series appeared in *The Public Advertiser* . Under the heading 'WORCESTER PORCELAIN', it read as follows:

'A Warehouse is opened at the Arts Museum, up one Pair of Stairs, in Cockspur Street, facing the Lower End of the Haymarket, with a great Variety of Articles at the said Manufactory, consisting of Table and Desert Services, Tea and Coffee Equipages and many other Articles, useful and ornamental, all enamelled, in Fruit, Flowers, Figures, Landscapes, etc. ornamented with Gold, which are to be sold, wholesale and retail, at the very lowest prices.

As the Enamelling Branch is performed in London under the immediate Direction of the Proprietor who has followed that Profession many Years, Ladies and Gentlemen will have their Orders executed with the greatest Dispatch, and painted to any Pattern they shall Chuse. Good Allowance to Merchants and Dealers'.

The name of the proprietor is not given in this first advertisement, nor in two identical insertions which appeared on 19th and 22nd December. However, a similarly worded advertisement on 8th January is headed , 'J. GILES, China and Enamel Painter', and adds that the 'great Variety of Articles' which were available for sale were 'curiously painted in the Dresden, Chelsea, and Chinese Tastes'.

Clearly Giles's main purpose in placing this advertisement was to announce the opening of his new shop 'at the Arts Museum, up one pair of Stairs, in Cockspur Street, facing the Lower End of the Haymarket'. As we have already seen, he is described as a 'Chinaman' in the 1747 list of voters, which makes it clear that he was already in the retailing business, but his new premises were in one of the most fashionable areas of mid-eighteenth century London and must have meant a substantial investment on his part. He would hardly have taken such a step unless his business was well established, and he was confident of further expansion.

In the meantime, however, on 19th December 1767 the Worcester Factory had also inserted an advertisement in *The Public Advertiser* which read as follows:-

'China. The chief Proprietor and acting Manager for the Proprietors of the Worcester Porcelain Manufactory having moved some thousand Pounds worth of their best Wares, from their Warehouse in the City, to the large Exhibition Room, Spring Gardens, Charing Cross, the chief Manager at the said Room, by Order of the said Proprietors, hath marked the lowest Prices on each Sample of the said ware, the same as at their Manufactory at Worcester, with the usual Discount to Traders. This Manufactory is more esteemed by real Judges than any other making in this Kingdom, being arrived at such great Beauty and Perfection. The Nobility and Gentry, who want particular Patterns of fine Goods made, are desired to leave their Orders in Time at the said Room, as the Reasonableness of the Prices makes them have so great a Demand, that they have now more to execute than they can perform for some Time'.

This was repeated on three occasions in the first half of January 1768, and then on 28th of the month, the Factory published the following, again in *The Public Advertiser*:-

'Exhibition Room, Spring Gardens, Charing Cross. As several of the Nobility and Gentry, etc. have lately been disappointed of seeing the large and curious Collection of the Worcester China Manufactory; as some of their Ware is advertised at another Room, painted in London, the chief Proprietor and acting Manager has sent some thousand Pounds Worth of the said Ware from their late Warehouse in Aldersgate-street, to be sold in the same Exhibition Room, where will be sent every week, new Variety of the finest Goods. Curious Patterns that are wanted will be made in a short Time not to be distinguished from the Original, as the Proprietors have engaged the best Painters from Chelsea etc. Any orders will be executed in the highest Taste, and much cheaper than can be afforded by any Painters in London. The said Goods are marked at the lowest Manufactory Prices in Worcester.'

This apparently hostile exchange of advertisements between Giles and the Factory has prompted much debate as to the precise relationship between the two at this time. Earlier writers had taken the view that although the reference to 'Worcester Porcelain' in the heading of Giles's advertisement suggested that he and the Factory had entered into some new commercial arrangement, the wording of the advertisements implied that they were still in competition. Gerald Coke also believed that Giles's advertisements indicated the start of a new agreement with the Factory. However, he went further and argued that in referring to the 'Enamelling Branch' being performed in London, Giles was saying, in effect, that he had taken over virtually the whole of the enamelling function from the Factory. This would have left it with only the simplest coloured and gilded patterns, together with its under-glaze blue and white and transfer-printed production.[10]

---

[10] Gerald Coke, op. cit. Chapter Two, *The Advertisements,* where the author argues that the advertisements and the activities of the Worcester Factory and Giles's workshop were complementary rather than competitive, and that Giles was literally 'the enamelling branch' of a joint venture with the Factory from 1767 until the arrangement was terminated in 1771.

However, there are no other grounds for believing that the Factory had agreed to such a radical arrangement, and it seems highly improbable that they should have done so.

The advertisements are ambiguous in some respects, but a close reading of them leaves little doubt that Giles and the Factory remained in competition, and subsequent writers have continued to take this view. The fact that they each had a showroom within yards of the other's - Giles at the Arts Museum in Cockspur Street, and the Factory at the Exhibition Room, Spring Gardens, Charing Cross - supports this, as Giles would hardly have incurred this expensive overhead if he had effectively been an employee of the Factory as Coke believed. Indeed, one can argue that Giles's advertising campaign and the opening of his new showroom were specifically aimed at increasing the competition against his rivals, chief of whom were the Worcester and Derby factories. The Chelsea factory had just closed, and Giles was quick to see the opportunity this gave him to establish his position at the top end of the market.

One must ask why, if that was the situation, the Factory continued to supply Giles with undecorated porcelain. They were not, however, in an easy situation: Giles was buying from them a substantial volume of porcelain on which, presumably, they made a profit. If they stopped supplying him, or raised the price to the point that he stopped buying, they would run the risk of losing this profit, and be forced to cut back production and lay off staff. In the meantime, Giles no doubt could find other sources of undecorated porcelain. Moreover, particularly during the first years of the 1770's, the Worcester Factory was going through a difficult period: the lease of its main site, Warmstry House, was coming to an end, the business was losing money, and in 1771 it was put up for sale. It changed hands in January 1772, and a new company was formed to manage it two months later. While these upheavals were going on the last thing the management wanted was to lose

one of its major purchasers. More positively they must have hoped that the association of their porcelain with Giles's decorating skills and reputation, would help them to penetrate the fashionable London market. Subsequent history suggests that they were right. By this time the Factory was producing porcelain of the highest quality, of simple but beautiful design, well potted and, unique among contemporary English factories, able to withstand heat without the body cracking or the glaze crazing. Clearly from Giles's standpoint, there was considerable advantage in exploiting the Worcester name in his advertisements. The fact is that Worcester's superb porcelain and Giles's outstanding skills as a decorator were a winning combination, which probably explains why what must have been an uneasy marriage continued until Giles started to withdraw from the decorating business in 1774.

By the late 1760's the marketing of porcelain in England had become a sophisticated process, and one of the several ways in which manufacturers made their products available to the retail and wholesale markets was sale by auction. Over the next four years three major sales of Worcester porcelain were held.

The first started on 4th May 1769 and lasted for nine days. It was conducted by Mr Burnsall in his auction room in Berkeley Square, and is important because in the advertisements in the run-up to the sale there is a description of the stock, and, in particular, a list of colours used. It consisted of 'complete Table and Desert Services, Leaves, Compotiers, Tea and Coffee Equipages…. in the beautiful colours of Mazarine Blue and Gold, Sky-blue, Pea-green, French-green, Sea-green, Purple, Scarlet, and other variety of Colours, richly decorated and with chased and burnished Gold….The whole enamelled in the highest Taste, and curiously painted in Figures, Birds, Landscapes, Flowers, Fruit, etc'. Gerald Coke[11] considered that the

---

[11] Gerald Coke, op. cit. page 36.

colours listed must refer to coloured grounds or borders, and that, because the Factory was not producing this wide range of ground colours at this stage, the sale must include Giles decorated wares. He went on to match the colours with those on surviving examples of Giles decorated wares. The description generally seems to match Giles's output better than that of the Factory, and the reference to 'chased and burnished Gold' sounds more like Giles's *cisisé* gilding than contemporary Factory gilding. However, in the first advertisement on 19th April, it is stated that the sale is 'by Order of the Proprietors of the Worcester Porcelain Manufactory', and that the stock is 'The large and very valuable Collection of the said Worcester Porcelain Manufactory'. A later insertion on 2nd May adds a note to the effect that 'The Proprietors of the aforesaid Porcelaine Manufactory beg leave to assure the Nobility, Gentry and others, that this is a genuine Sale, and nothing introduced but what is their Property'. This appears to make it clear that the sale consisted exclusively of Factory decorated services. A possible, but not entirely satisfactory, explanation is that the list of colours refers not to coloured grounds or borders, but simply details those used by the Factory in its polychrome decoration.

In the same year, another sale of 'A Large and elegant Assortment of the WORCESTER PORCELAINE', as it was described in *The Public Advertiser,* was held at Christie's on 13th December and the five following days. The catalogue for this sale has survived, but the descriptions of the lots are, on the whole, too brief and too vague to be of any real value in terms of making positive identifications of either Giles or Factory patterns.

A third sale was advertised in *The Public Advertiser* on 1st May 1770. It was to be held on the following and subsequent days, 'at the large warehouse in Cockspur-street'. This was made up of 'ALL the genuine and valuable Stock of Worcester China.... The Whole consisting of elegant Desert Services, fine Tea Sets, Caudles,

Covers and Stands, Baskets, Leaves, and Compotiers, etc. curiously enamelled in Figures, Birds, Flowers, etc. and ornamented with Mazarine and Sky Blue and Gold'. It goes on to state that 'Every Article in this Sale is the sole Property, and has been enamelled in London by and under the Direction of the Proprietor of the said warehouse'. Although his name is not mentioned, this clearly refers to Giles, and confirms, in broad terms, the objects he was decorating and the types of decoration he was applying.

In June 1771 Giles gave up his showroom in the Arts Museum in Cockspur Street and took a new lease on a shop, also in Cockspur Street. Gerald Coke[12] believed that this was occasioned by the termination of the agreement whereby Giles acted as 'the enamelling branch' of the Worcester Factory, but, as has been argued above, whatever agreement there may have been between the two was almost certainly a much more limited affair. The fact that Giles continued to buy large quantities of undecorated porcelain from the Factory until 1774 suggests that there was no radical change in their relationship.

Giles's ledger[13] for the period from the middle of 1771 to 1776 has survived and throws some light on his business during these last five years of its existence. It appears to have been used to record any transactions where credit was extended, either to customers or by suppliers. The bulk of the entries refer to the former, and most read something like 'A parcel China sold & del'd', ie 'delivered'. This suggests that when an order was taken, it was recorded in an order book, and then when the items were delivered, it was entered in the ledger, and subsequent payments credited to the account. Only the first seventy-three folios of the ledger - about a third of its capacity - have been used.

---

[12] Gerald Coke, op. cit. page 5.
[13] Now in the Toppin Library of the English Ceramic Circle.

At the beginning of the ledger is an alphabetical index in which are entered the names of Giles's customers and his suppliers. The list of customers makes it clear that Giles was still dealing with the very top end of the market: those under the letter 'A' set the tone - Lady Abingdon, Lady Ailesford, Princess Amelia (the second daughter of George II), The 'Dutchess' of Ancaster, and Lady Ancram. The number of his customers listed is nearly two hundred, of whom a quarter are titled.

The list of suppliers shows that, in addition to the large quantities of undecorated porcelain which Giles continued to buy from the Worcester Factory, he was also supplied with 'blue' china, which in this context meant porcelain which had been partly decorated with under-glaze blue grounds. The ledger also shows that Giles bought parcels of china which are described as 'blue and white', and clearly distinguished from other 'blue' and other 'white' porcelain bought at the same time. This must have been finished, Factory decorated, under-glaze blue and white porcelain, ready for sale, and during 1774 he also purchased a small number of parcels of 'Enameld' china, which, again, must have been Factory decorated wares bought as stock for his shop.

Giles's last purchase from Worcester was in December 1774 and at the end of the year he owed the Factory £484-4-0. He made a series of small cash payments during 1775 and by September the amount outstanding had been reduced to £249-4-0, which was settled by two bills: one for £49-4-0 at 3 months and one for £200 at 6 months, suggesting that by this time Giles's was suffering from cash flow problems.

The ledger also shows that Giles bought china from William Duesbury, the proprietor of the Derby Factory who had taken over the Chelsea Factory in 1768, but it is probable that all this porcelain was finished and ready for sale. Other suppliers mentioned in the ledger were Philip Christian's Liverpool factory and Thomas

Turner, whose accounts will be discussed in more detail in Chapter 3.

The ledger shows that from 1771 until 1775 Giles had dealings with Charles Vere who was based in Fleet Street, and ran a very substantial wholesale business in china, glass, tea, snuff and other products imported from the East. In addition Giles had accounts with Stephen Hall & Co. and William Parker from both of whom he purchased glass during 1771 and 1772. It is clear from the substantial quantities of finished china and glass that Giles bought from his suppliers, that at this stage of his career the retail side was a very important part of his business.

Although the ledger records only part of Giles's activity, it does give an indication of the state of the business over the five years it covers. The annual figures of Giles's purchases of porcelain from the Worcester Factory show a high level from 1771 through 1773, followed by a sharp decline in 1774, and a similar pattern is indicated by an annual figure for 'enamelling' - payments from Giles's retail business to his enamelling branch. These show that up until 1774 the business continued to trade at a high level, but in that year it started to contract quite rapidly.

This picture is supported by the fact that in March 1774 Christie's held a sale made up entirely of Giles's stock. Unlike the previous sales it was not advertised in *The Public Advertiser*, but the introduction to the catalogue[14] describes it as 'A CATALOGUE of the Elegant Porcelaine Of English and Foreign Manufacture, Part of the STOCK in TRADE of Mr. *JAMES GILES*, CHINAMAN and ENAMELLER, Quitting that Business; brought from his shop in *Cockspur Street*, opposite *Spring Gardens*.' The catalogue describes the various lots in some detail, and is the best documentary evidence we have in terms of

---

[14] Reprinted in full in Gerald Coke's *In Search of James Giles*, Appendix G.

identifying Giles's patterns. For example, lot 57 on the fifth and final day of the sale is 'a desert service elegantly painted with different vases and an ultramarine blue border, enriched with chased and burnished gold, 24 plates, sundry compoteers and 5 baskets'. This description fits two of Giles's well known services painted with urns within a blue border enriched with bunches of grapes and vine leaves in gold (nos. 83 and 84).

The sale lasted for five days and there were 90 lots each day, a total of 450 lots. A number are attributed to Continental factories in their descriptions: 'a compleat set of Nymphenbourg tea china' for example. About 40 lots are described as 'Chelsea', and the bulk of the lots have no factory ascribed to them. R J Charleston has suggested[15] that much of this is Chelsea-Derby porcelain, bought at auction by Giles and, like those lots described as 'Chelsea', already decorated and ready for sale. R J Charleston also pointed out that 50 lots - more than ten percent of the total - were glass, some of which was probably decorated by Giles. There were also a number of biscuit figures and some pieces of blue and white which clearly were not decorated by him. Unfortunately, there is not enough information to make an accurate assessment of what proportion of the lots were wares decorated in the Giles workshop and how much was retail stock bought by him in a finished state ready for sale.

Despite the preamble to the 1774 sale describing Giles as 'Quitting that Business', the ledger shows that he continued to trade for another two years, and indeed there are half a dozen entries in 1777, the latest in September of that year, - all cash settlements by customers of overdue bills. An entry in *The Public Advertiser* dated 3rd January 1776 announced that Giles was giving up his Cockspur Street premises and 'removed' to his manufactory in Soho. Then in March and April of the same year a series of advertisements in *The Morning Post* and *The Daily Advertiser* announced the sale by auction by Mr Squibb of 'the elegant and valuable stock of Mr Giles, Chinaman and Enameller'. By this time Giles was in his late fifties, and he may have been content to call it a day.

Some indication of the size of Giles's business is given by the value of his fire insurance. Thanks to the researches of Mrs Elizabeth Adams[16] into the records of the Sun Assurance Company we know that Giles took out a policy on 14th August 1771 when his Utensils and Stock were valued at £2,000. A subsequent policy dated 6th November 1772 shows that the value of his stock ('Glass, China and Earthenware included') had reached what Mrs Adams calls 'the prodigious value of £2,500'. An insurance policy for the Worcester Factory makes an interesting comparison. This is dated April 1772, and is also with the Sun Company. The Factory's buildings are valued at £560, while the 'Utensils and Stock' are put at £680. In September of the following year the stock of china held in the Factory's City warehouse at 12 Gough Square, Fleet Street was valued at £800. At this date Worcester was one of the largest of the English porcelain manufacturers, and the fact that the value of its stock at the Factory and in its London warehouse together was only about sixty percent of that of Giles's stock indicates what a substantial business the latter had become.

The 1763 advertisement in Thomas Mortimer's *The Universal Director*, describes Giles as 'This ingenious Artist' who 'copies the Pattern of any China with the utmost exactness'. This strongly suggests that at this stage Giles was himself actively engaged in the decorating of porcelain. An advertisement in *The Public Advertiser* seven years later, however, mentions that Giles 'may be spoke with daily at the above Warehouse' ie

[15] R J Charleston, *ECC Transactions*, Vol. 6, Part 3, page 295.

[16] Elizabeth Adams, *ECC Transactions*, Vol. 10, Part 1, page 16.

the shop in Cockspur Street which he opened in 1767. Clearly, if he was available to 'be spoke with' there daily, he could not have spent much time decorating china and glass in his workshop in Soho: indeed, when he was in Soho he must have spent all his time overseeing what was by then a large undertaking. We know[17] also that in the early 1770's he was buying large quantities of finished china both at auction and direct from the manufacturers, all of which suggests that from 1767 his attention was more on the retail side of his business than on the decorating side. As a result he must have done little decorating himself, if any.

Of Giles domestic life we know only the barest facts. As we have seen, he was born in 1718, and according to his apprenticeship record his father was of St. Giles in the Fields, but there is no record of his birth in that parish. Giles's wife was named Mary but we know nothing of her or when she and Giles were married. They had two daughters, the eldest of whom, also Mary, was born in 1741. In 1763 she married John Hall who was a well-known engraver, and they lived for some time at 83, Berwick Street, close to James Giles, who lived in Berwick Street in the same premises as his business for the whole of his adult life. Giles's second daughter, Sarah Teresa, was born in 1742. She was a miniature painter and there exists a portrait of her father which she painted. Both Giles's daughters may have worked in their father's enamelling business.

James Giles died on 8th August 1780 and was buried in the family vault in Paddington Old Churchyard ten days later. No will of his has been traced.

---

[17] R J Charleston, *ECC Transactions,* Vol.6, Part 3, page 296.

Until the appearance of the 'Grubbe' plates in 1935, ceramic historians' knowledge of James Giles and of his association with the Worcester Factory was confined to the various references in the advertisements and sale catalogues which were discussed in Chapter 1. There was no real evidence with which to distinguish between the porcelain decorated in his workshop and that decorated by the Factory. The situation changed in 1935 when Mrs Dora Edgell Grubbe, the widow of a direct descendant of Giles, presented to the Victoria and Albert Museum the four plates which have since borne her name. Although there remain a number of unanswered questions relating to the plates, there seems to be no doubt that they were decorated in Giles's workshop. Nearly twenty years later, a pair of tea canisters with a similar history were sold by another member of the family, and by using the decorative features of the plates and the tea canisters, ceramic historians have been able to identify a large part of the output of the Giles workshop, and in particular to distinguish between his and Factory decoration on Worcester porcelain. Chapter 5 contains a list of Giles features - flowers, fruit, gilding etc, which were regularly used by the workshop in its decoration. Some of these are to be found on the Grubbe plates and canisters themselves, while the others are linked to them via the decoration of intermediate objects.

The plates were accepted on behalf of the Museum by Mr W B Honey, the Keeper of the Department of Ceramics at the time, and in a subsequent paper[1] read to the English Ceramic Circle he described them, and repeated Mrs Grubbe's account of their history, as follows:

'The plates are undoubtedly Worcester, though somewhat imperfect and out of shape. Now Mrs Grubbe stated that the family tradition regarding the plates is that they were specially made by a John Giles .... for the wedding of his daughter Mary Giles, who married John Hall, an ancestor of the Grubbes'.

Mr Honey went on to say that 'Mrs Grubbe has stated that Mary Giles married John Hall about 1785'.

Mrs Grubbe was the second wife of a Mr Walter Grubbe who was a direct descendant of James Giles, and by the time she presented the plates to the Museum her husband had died. It is not, therefore, surprising that she gave the first name of her late husband's ancestor as 'John' instead of 'James'. She was also mistaken about the date of Mary Giles's wedding, since thanks to the research of Major Tapp[2] it is now known that this took place in 1763, and not in 1785 as Mrs Grubbe thought.

Most authorities[3] have taken the view that the plates and their decoration are of later date than 1763, the year of Mary's marriage to John Hall. As regards the decoration, the Chelsea factory was painting services with landscape scenes in green and carmine monochrome in the 1750's, and the style of decoration on Plates 3 and 4 is found on Continental porcelain of the same period. In his 1763 advertisement in The Universal Director, Giles claimed to 'copy the Pattern of any China with the utmost exactness', and the actual decoration of the plates could, therefore, have been carried out by 1763. However, this shape of plate was not introduced by Worcester until the middle of the 1760s, and it is, thus, unlikely that they could have been manufactured at Worcester and painted in the Giles workshop in time for Mary's wedding.

---

[1] The Work of James Giles; W.B.Honey, E.C.C.Transactions, Vol.1, part 5, page 14.

[2] E.C.C.Transactions, op.cit., page 15.
[3] E.C.C.Transactions, op.cit., page 15.
Gerald Coke; op.cit., page 52.

In any case, four plates, each decorated in an entirely different fashion, seem an unlikely wedding present. By 1763 Giles was an established and successful businessman, and one can understand his wanting to give his daughter something decorated in his own workshop on the occasion of her marriage. However, if he were to do so, it seems much more likely that he would have given her a complete service which she and her husband could have used, or, alternatively, something decorative such as a garniture of vases. On the face of it, it seems highly improbable that he would have given her four unmatching plates, especially since the plates themselves were 'somewhat imperfect and out of shape'.

The two Grubbe landscape plates appear to be from matching services, other examples of which are in public or private collections, and one of which is no. 109 in this exhibition. This raises the question as to how - assuming they were not a wedding present - one plate from each service should have remained in the possession of Giles's family, while the others are, presumably, survivors from services which had been sold to his customers. One possible explanation is that when Giles decorated these services, he painted an extra plate above the number ordered. This could have been either to provide a replacement in case of damage during the various subsequent processes of firing, gilding and delivery, or as a sample for other prospective customers: the latter explanation being perhaps the more likely. Thus all four Grubbe plates may originally have been spares or samples which had been retained in the workshop. When he wound up his business in 1776, Giles may well have decided to keep them, especially if he had painted any of them himself. On his death they would have passed to his daughter, Mary, and eventually to Mrs Grubbe.

This raises the question as to whether the plates were painted by Giles himself, or whether they were simply the work of painters in his workshop. Some authorities have considered that they were all Giles's work. In his catalogue of the Klepser Collection, for example, Simon Spero[4] states that, 'It is generally accepted that these plates were painted by Giles'. Gerald Coke cites family tradition as supporting the case for Giles's authorship, and, referring to W B Honey's paper to the English Ceramic Circle quoted above, states that, 'According to Mr Honey Mrs Dora Grubbe was quite satisfied that the plates which she presented to the Museum were decorated by her husband's ancestor, James Giles.'[5] According to Honey, however, what Mrs Grubbe actually said was that the plates were 'specially made by John Giles', which is not quite the same thing, and could mean no more than that Giles had made a special order for them. In any case we have already seen that Mrs Grubbe's testimony is unreliable in other respects. A related question is whether all four plates are painted by the same hand. W B Honey believed that they were,[6] but Dr Bernard Watney considered that Plate 4 was the work of Fidelle Duvivier, a freelance decorator who may have made use of Giles's facilities but was probably not an employee.[7] It is also open to question as to whether Plates 1 and 2 were painted by the same hand. The landscape painting on the latter is of high quality and the scene clearly depicted, while that on Plate 1 - admittedly using a different technique - is somewhat obscure, and certainly inferior in quality to that on the other green landscape services at Saltram House and Corsham Court. On balance the evidence is against Giles having painted all four plates himself, though it is possible that he may have painted some of them.

There is another uncertainty. About the year 1900 a friend of the Grubbe family drew up a family tree tracing their ancestry back to John

---

[4] S. Spero; The Klepser Collection, Ch. VI, page 129.
[5] E.C.C.Transactions, op.cit., page 14.
[6] E.C.C.Transactions, op.cit, page 15.
[7] Dr B.Watney; E.C.C.Transactions, Vol. 14, Pt 3, page 251.

and Mary Hall. At the same time he produced an inventory of the family's possessions which he illustrated with water colour paintings and photographs of the more important items. This included a considerable body of porcelain, mainly Oriental, but also some Meissen, and some pieces of Factory-decorated Worcester, as well as the four Grubbe plates and the two tea canisters which will be descibed later. The question arises as to whether, in among the other Factory decorated pieces, it is plausible to assume that the six pieces allegedly decorated in Giles's workshop should have remained separate in the minds of the family over a number of generations. In other words, can we trust the family tradition that these particular pieces were decorated in the workshop? A partial answer may be that four of them, Plates 2 and 4, and the two canisters are more prominently illustrated than any of the other porcelain items, which might suggest that the compiler was aware of their special importance to the family.

Nevertheless, despite these uncertainties about the history and the authenticity of the plates, there is agreement among students of Giles's work that they were decorated in his workshop. Turning to the plates themselves, the first feature to note is that they are all of the same twelve-lobed shape, a form derived from Meissen.

Looking at the individual plates in turn, Plate 1 has a landscape scene in the well. It is outlined and highlighted in black, and washed over in green. It shows a woman and a child standing in front of a large urn on a plinth, and there are cattle, buildings and trees in the background. Inside the irregular gilt rim there is a distinctive and elaborate gilt border, which is probably unique to the Giles workshop, and which is found on a number of items of both Chinese and Worcester porcelain which have been attributed to the workshop[8]. It is also found on some Giles-decorated glass.

_____

[8] Bonhams; Zorensky Collection, Pt.II, lot 227.

Plate 2 is also painted with a landscape scene, this time in carmine. The scene is of a man and a woman standing before a cistern beside columns and broken masonry. In front of them is a dog and in the background there are buildings and mountains. Inside the gilt rim there is a border, made up of individual flower sprays, also in carmine. At least ten similarly painted plates are known, but as in the case of Plate 1 it is the border decoration which is most revealing in terms of identifying Giles's work, since these flowers are recurring motifs of Giles decoration, both in colour and, as here, in monochrome. The convolvulus at five o'clock, and the auricula at twelve o'clock, in particular, are common Giles features.

Plate 3 is, however, the most valuable in terms of recognising Giles's work. Like the other plates it has a gilt rim, and from this is suspended an irregular border, with three cornucopia-shaped peaks which extend into the well. It is edged with a series of gilt rococo 'c' scrolls. This particular shape of border, which was again inspired by Meissen, is different from that used by the Worcester factory, or, indeed, by any other contemporary English factory. The blue and red scale ground found on this plate is otherwise unrecorded, but this distinctive border shape and gilt outline were employed by Giles in conjunction with a number of different ground colours, both scale and plain.

The other decoration on this plate is also important. A central bouquet of flowers and fruit, including a piece of cut fruit, together with scattered individual flowers and fruit, is a decorative combination frequently used by Giles and is once more of Meissen origin. The use of a convolvulus with a trailing tendril has already been noted in conjunction with the flower border on Plate 2. The red auricula and the forget-me-nots are equally common Giles flowers, and the pair of mushrooms, one in profile and the other painted so that its pleated underside is visible, is a favourite Giles device. Finally the overall disposition of the decoration should be noted:

Grubbe plate 1

Grubbe plate 2

Grubbe plate 3

Grubbe plate 4

Figure 1, All Courtesy of the Victoria and Albert Museum

the main bouquet has been placed slightly off-centre and the four subsidiary sprays are not at ninety degrees to each other, giving an effect of freedom and informality which tends to be lacking in similarly decorated Factory wares of this period.

Unfortunately, Plate 4 is a maverick. Its decoration appears to be unique on English porcelain, and provides no help in identifying Giles's other work. It consists of two dead geese hanging on a tree stump in the centre, while around the rim are three groups of dead game and shot guns, suspended from green swags.

In 1952 Miss M. J. M. Grubbe, a niece of Mrs Dora Grubbe, sold at Sotheby's the pair of tea canisters, which had also been handed down within the family and whose decoration was also traditionally held to be the work of her ancestor James Giles. As already noted, like two of the Grubbe plates, they were prominently illustrated in the inventory of the family's possessions drawn up about 1900. The decoration on the canisters is similar and they were obviously intended as a pair. One is in the Marshall Collection in the Ashmolean Museum at Oxford and is no. 92 in this exhibition, and the other was in the Gerald Coke Collection which is now in the Museum of Worcester Porcelain, figure 2.

Each canister has two large cartouches and four small ones reserved against an under-glaze blue ground, which is richly decorated with *ciselé* gilding. In one of the large reserves there is a Teniers-type figure, while the reverse is painted with a cluster of fruit and flowers. There are flowers also in the small panels, elaborate gilding round the neck, and a gold band around the foot-rim. Neither canister has its cover, and there is no other known piece of porcelain which has the same decorative combination of Teniers-type figures in cartouches reserved against a

Fig. 2 The Grubbe tea canister at Museum of Worcester Porcelain, courtesy of the Museum of Worcester Porcelain.

scale-blue ground. This suggests that, like Plates 3 and 4, the canisters were sample or experimental pieces which were never marketed in complete services. The importance of the canisters is that they associate this type of figure painting with the Giles workshop, as well as the *ciselé* gilding which is one of the most distinctive, as well as one of the most sumptuous features of Giles decoration.

It has been suggested in Chapter 1 that after James Giles had completed his apprenticeship in 1740, he may have gone to work in one of the outside decorating workshops in London, where he acquired the skills of china decoration. We now know that he had probably set up his own workshop by 1743. The 1763 entry in Mortimer's *The Universal Director* describes him as having 'followed that Profession many Years', and by that date his business was clearly well established.

During the early years of his career Giles's source of porcelain was Chinese. This had been imported undecorated by the East India Company from the 1720's, and distributed by a number of different firms, including Margas & Co, whose proprietor, Philip Margas, was master to Giles's elder brother, Abraham, during the latter's apprenticeship. The exhibition includes a number of pieces of Chinese porcelain with decoration attributed to the Giles workshop: all are useful wares, and include a pair of plates and various items from tea and coffee services.

A feature of this Chinese porcelain is that while the tea bowls and saucers are finely potted, the coffee cups and milk jugs are heavy in comparison, and fitted with rather crude handles. Simon Spero has suggested that the reason for this was that the latter objects had to be ordered specially for the European market, and the Chinese potters had no experience of putting handles on small objects like coffee cups and jugs. They therefore potted them more heavily in order to support the handles. They may also have been more expensive to import because the handles would prevent their being stacked like saucers and bowls, and they would have taken up more space in the ships' holds. The high cost and the comparatively poor quality of Chinese coffee cups and jugs may have been the reasons why Giles turned to the Worcester Factory for his undecorated porcelain.

The evidence for this is the existence of a small number of so-called 'mixed services', ie made up of items of both Chinese and Worcester porcelain. A good example is a part tea and coffee service which was sold at Puttick and Simpson's in 1963, in which the milk jug and six coffee cups are of Worcester porcelain, while the teapot, nine tea bowls and four saucers are of Chinese porcelain. All are clearly from the same service, and decorated with Teniers-type figures, an example of which is also found on the Grubbe tea canister, no. 92. A Chinese saucer and a Worcester coffee cup which may have come from this service are no. 88 in the exhibition. Examples of 'mixed services' also occur with green landscape decoration, no. 106, and with fancy bird decoration. By combining traditional Chinese objects like tea bowls, saucers and tea canisters with Worcester manufactured coffee cups and jugs, Giles could claim to be giving his customers the best of both sources.

Giles's mixed services may, therefore, represent his earliest use of Worcester porcelain and are probably dated about 1760. To about the same period may be attributed a group of mugs, whose principal decoration is usually enclosed within a barbed panel edged with narrow black and red lines, nos. 56 and 107. The decoration will be examined in more detail in the next chapter, but the mugs themselves may be either cylindrical or bell-shaped, and are also found in two sizes - the examples in this exhibition are of the larger size. Curiously, apart from two pairs of mugs with armorial decoration (that with the arms of Martindale is no. 80), mugs are objects which scarcely feature in Giles's subsequent output.

The decoration on some Bow porcelain has also been attributed to the Giles workshop, and his use of this factory's porcelain probably also dates from the first half of the 1760's. The exhibition includes a plate which is certainly Bow, no. 63 and a pair of vases which are possibly Bow, no. 89. Both have factory applied under-glaze blue grounds, and it is possible that Giles bought from Bow because it could supply him with these part decorated wares which were not available on Chinese porcelain, and not yet available on Worcester.

The plate has an anchor and dagger mark in red, and it was thought at one time that this mark was indicative of Giles decoration on Bow. However, there exists a number of objects bearing this mark whose decoration was almost certainly not applied in the Giles workshop. It was the practice at the Bow factory to farm out some of its decoration, and a possible explanation of the dagger and anchor mark is that it was used by Bow to indicate all outside decoration, including that done in the Giles workshop[1]. In this case Giles would have been a sub-contractor to the Bow factory, a quite different relationship from that which he subsequently had with the Worcester factory, from whom he bought porcelain, decorated it and then sold it on at his own risk.

By 1767, when Giles was heading his advertisements in *The Public Advertiser* WORCESTER PORCELAIN, it can reasonably be assumed that he was buying virtually all his undecorated porcelain from that source, and he had probably switched to the factory as his main supplier some years before that date.

From the Christie's 1774 sale catalogue we can deduce the composition of the services which Giles was buying from the Worcester Factory. 'A complete tea set china' consisted of thirty-nine to forty-one pieces, made up of twelve teacups and saucers, six coffee cups, a teapot and stand, a milk jug with cover, a cream jug, one or two tea canisters, a sugar bowl, a slop basin, a coffee pot, a spoon tray, and one or two saucer dishes or 'bread and butter plates'. 'A

---

[1]See Elizabeth Adams & David Redstone, *Bow Porcelain,* pages 184-187 for a full discussion of this question.

desert service' was more variable in its make-up. Plates came in dozen or half dozen units, and in two different regular sizes: one of nine inches diameter with a wavy rim of twelve indentations, and a smaller, eight inch diameter version with a scalloped rim and twenty-four indentations. Both Giles and the Factory used each version for their finished services, but, on the basis of what has survived, Giles evidently favoured the larger plate and the Factory the smaller one. A service also included baskets and various shapes of dish, or 'compoteer' to use the contemporary term. For example, lot 76 on the last day of the 1774 sale is described as 'a desert service with basket work brim, consisting of 18 plates, 1 large basket, 4 small ditto and 14 sundry shaped compoteers'. Another service sold on the same day was made up of '24 plates, 7 compoteers and 4 baskets'. The most usual forms of compoteer are square and lozenge-shaped dishes, which come in two different sizes, and a heart-shaped dish, which appears to have been made in one size only. Examples of all of these are in the exhibition, together with two sizes of basket.

In addition to the various components of tea and dessert services, Giles also bought a wide range of other useful wares. These include 'caudle cups, covers and stands', 'chocolate cups and saucers', butter tubs, covers and stands, 'large breakfast cups and saucers', 'cream basons, covers and plates', 'ice cream cups', 'sauce boats', 'colliflower leaves', and 'vine leaves'. These were sold in pairs or sixes as appropriate, and examples of most are in the exhibition, though not always easy to distinguish - the difference between a caudle cup and a chocolate cup, for example, is by no means clear. Curiously, although sauce boats are mentioned and are relatively common objects, no Worcester examples with Giles workshop decoration have been identified. The 1774 sale catalogue included a whole range of other objects, but most of these were probably from Giles's retail business and bought in from different suppliers already decorated. Purely decorative items bought from Worcester include the large hexagonal vases, which are known in a number of different Giles patterns.

Much of the porcelain purchased by Giles from the Worcester factory was part decorated with under-glaze blue grounds. Indeed, during the period from 27th July 1772 when the ledger first distinguished between the two, until the end of 1774 when Giles stopped buying from the Factory, his purchases of 'white China' and 'blue' were almost exactly equal in value. Presumably the unit cost of the part decorated wares was higher than that of the white, so that, unless there was a huge differential in price, perhaps as much as a third of the porcelain he bought from Worcester during this period was part-decorated with under-glaze blue grounds.

These were introduced by the Worcester Factory in the mid-1760's. There were three different types - powder blue, solid or 'wet' blue, and scale blue. The first is very rarely found on Giles decorated wares, and one of the few, if not only, examples recorded is a tea service decorated with musicians in the style of Watteau. The sugar bowl from this service is no. 90. The type most commonly used by Giles is the scale blue ground, a form of decoration invented by the Worcester Factory. As applied to flat, circular objects like saucers and plates, the most usual version of this type of ground has a circular reserved panel in the centre, surrounded by three, large mirror-shaped panels, with smaller panels in between them, and three pairs of narrow, triangular panels round the rim. Panels of the same shapes, suitably modified and reduced in number, were used on other objects like teapots and cups. Giles used this format with flower, no. 19, and bird decoration, no. 66, in the panels and rich *ciselé* gilding on the blue ground. The effect is sumptuous, but somewhat crowded, and possibly for this reason Giles may have asked the Factory to produce for him a version with a much simplified arrangement of panels. Instead of thirteen panels this has only four - three mirror-shaped with a circular panel

in the centre. Giles used this format for two versions of the Lady Mary Wortley Montagu pattern, where the fewer panels and larger areas of blue scale ground show his gilding to dazzling effect, no. 64. The Factory does not appear to have used this arrangement of panels for its finished services.

Giles's use of wet or solid blue is confined to broad borders on dessert plates - an example is no. 84, from a service painted with different urns in the centre, and with a blue border richly decorated with bunches of grapes and vine leaves in gold.

Much of the undecorated porcelain bought by Giles from the Worcester Factory bore a factory mark painted in under-glaze blue on the back or base of the object. The question of marks on First Period Worcester porcelain was examined in depth in a study by Mr S M Clarke whose findings were published in a Bulletin of the American Ceramic Circle[2]. Mr Clarke's conclusions were based on the descriptions of the marks on the on-glaze decorated objects in H R Marshall's *Coloured Worcester Porcelain of the First Period*, the published catalogues of various well-known collections including the Schreiber and Klepser Collections, and a number of Sotheby's sale catalogues. This was a total of 4,489 items, both Factory and Giles decorated - an 'item' in this context being, for instance, a teapot and cover, or a cup and saucer, or one lot in a sale catalogue.

Many of the tea wares decorated in the Giles workshop carry the Meissen crossed swords mark with the addition of the numeral *9* and a dot. It appears on teacups and saucers, more rarely on coffee cups and other tea wares, though never on teapot stands or spoon trays. Of the 4,489 items in Mr Clarke's study, 136 have the crossed swords mark, and he attributes forty-five to fifty of these to the Giles workshop.

---

[2] American Ceramic Circle Bulletin / Number 2, pages 63-75.

According to Gerald Coke[3], however, of the 'twenty-six pieces illustrated in Marshall which carry the Meissen mark, twenty-three can be assigned to Giles on grounds other than the mark, two are possibly by him, and only one, according to our present knowledge, should be attributed to the Factory'. On this evidence one might conclude that the Meissen mark was added at Giles's instigation, but this seems unlikely as it first appears on Factory decorated pieces as early as 1758-60[4]. What is certain is that it was applied to objects whose shape was based on a Meissen model, though whether in order 'to add spurious authenticity to certain shapes ....made in imitation of Meissen .... wares', as Mr Clarke believed, or for some other reason, is obscure.

The other factory marks found on Giles-decorated objects are the fretted square and the crescent. One or other of these invariably appears on pieces which are also partly decorated with Factory applied under-glaze blue scale or wet blue grounds or borders. The square mark also appears on tea wares which have no other Factory applied decoration, but have fluted sides, with scalloped or barbed edges to the cups, saucers, saucer dishes and bowls. In his paper Mr Clarke demonstrates that these marks were not used concurrently, but that the square was applied during the period from about 1765-75, and the crescent from about 1775-80.

Giles decoration is also found on the porcelain of some of the other English factories and, in some cases, dealings with the factory concerned are recorded in the ledger. Thus one entry shows that on 26th August 1771 Giles bought 'a parcel of white China' to the value of £25:10:3 from Philip Christian's Liverpool factory. Dr Bernard

Watney had identified several pieces of Christian's tea ware which have Giles decoration, one of which is a tea bowl with dry blue flower painting in this exhibition, no. 32[5]. Giles also had dealings with Thomas Turner which are recorded in the ledger. Up until June 1775 Turner is described as 'at Worcester', and after that date as 'at Caughley'. In the earlier period he was supplying 'Worcester China' on sale or return, which were most probably finished goods, but in the later period he is selling Giles 'Salopian White' ie. undecorated Caughley porcelain. Only one parcel to the value of £6:2:6 is, however, recorded.

Some Pennington's Liverpool punch bowls, no. 118, and tea wares have fruit and flower decoration which has been attributed to the Giles workshop, but there is no record in the ledger of Giles buying blanks from this source. Similar fruit painting is found on Chelsea-Derby plates, no. 117, which Gerald Coke attributed to the Giles workshop, but they also show a number of features otherwise not found on Giles decorated objects. Some pieces of Vauxhall porcelain[6] were unquestionably decorated by Giles, but the very small number that has survived suggests that this factory was not a regular supplier. This is probably true, too, of the Liverpool factories and Caughley, whom Giles may have bought from in small quantities simply to try out as possible alternative suppliers to Worcester.

---

[3] Gerald Coke, op. cit., page 31.
[4] For example, the tea service bearing the arms of Hayward with Parsons in pretence, from which a teacup, a coffee cup and a saucer are illustrated in Simon Spero & John Sandon, *Worcester Porcelain, The Zorensky Collection*, no. 107.

[5] Dr Bernard Watney, *ECC Transactions*, Vol.14, part 3, page 249, *James Giles and Liverpool Porcelain*.
[6] A small baluster shaped Vauxhall mug decorated with typical Giles fruit and flowers within panels reserved against a powder blue ground is illustrated in the Albert Amor 2002 Autumn Exhibition Catalogue, no. 41.

In his book on James Giles, Gerald Coke states that, 'as far as the Giles *atelier* is concerned, …. I do not think that there is any value in dating any piece and none is dated in this monograph.'[1] In his support he cites the fact that H R Marshall dated none of the pieces in Part II of his *Coloured Worcester Porcelain of the First Period.* Coke also argues that dating has 'distinct limitations', since the Giles workshop 'was only actively in business for about thirteen years'. Thanks to the research of Roger Massey discussed in Chapter I, we now know that the workshop may have been in existence for as much as thirty years, and for this reason, and the fact that later authorities have generally applied dates to Giles's work, it seems appropriate to attempt to do so here, or at least try to put his various decorative styles into chronological order.

Some indication of the difficulty of dating Giles decoration is given by the fact that of the forty six pieces in the Catalogue of The Zorensky Collection[2] attributed to the workshop, forty one, or just over ninety percent, are dated to the four year period 1768-72. This four year span may well have covered the peak of Giles's production, but his workshop was decorating Worcester porcelain for a period of possibly fifteen years, and it seems unlikely that so much of its output should have been concentrated in the short period that these figures suggest.

As we have seen in Chapter 1, Giles probably set up his own decorating workshop in Soho as early as 1743, based on the use of Chinese porcelain. The Watney collection included a number of pieces of Chinese porcelain with decoration attributed to the workshop, but the earliest of these is the pair of plates, no. 75, which were dated 'circa 1755' in the catalogue

of the sale[3]. No decoration before that date has been positively attributed to Giles, but in the early years of the workshop the output must have been small, and very little may have survived.

The exhibition also includes about a dozen other pieces of Chinese porcelain painted with flowers, fancy birds, green landscape scenes and armorial decoration, all of which show similarities in style to early Giles decoration on Worcester. On this basis they have been tentatively dated between 1755 and 1763. In addition there are the Chinese porcelain components of the mixed Chinese and Worcester tea services. Giles may well have continued to decorate stocks of unused Chinese porcelain after he had switched to Worcester as his supplier, but it seems unlikely that this would have continued beyond the mid-1760s, and there is no evidence of his decorating Chinese porcelain after that date[4].

From 1767, when Giles's first advertisement headed 'Worcester Porcelain' appeared, the Factory must have been his principal and probably sole supplier. This is confirmed by the ledger which shows that he was buying undecorated and part decorated porcelain almost exclusively from Worcester from 1771 until 1774. What is unclear, however, is whether Giles was already buying Worcester porcelain in quantity before 1767, and, if so, when he started

[1] Gerald Coke, op. cit. page 30.
[2] Simon Spero and John Sandon, *Worcester Porcelain, The Zorensky Collection,* Chapter 12.

[3] Phillips' sale of the Watney Collection, Part III, 1st November 2000, lot 811.
[4] In the catalogue of the 1983 Albert Amor exhibition, *The Elegant Porcelain of James Giles,* no. 13, it is suggested that the mixed services probably date 'from 1771 to the closure of the atelier'. This was based on the assumption that after the termination of the 'agreement' with the Factory in 1771, Giles had difficulty in obtaining Worcester blanks. However, it is clear from the ledger that he continued to buy from the Factory in large quantities until 1774.

to do so. John Sandon[5] suggests that 'The earliest Worcester porcelain which is stylistically linkable to Giles appears to be from the early to mid-1760s', which makes it puzzling that so little Giles decorated Worcester has hitherto been attributed to the period prior to 1767.

There are, however, a number of services which suggest that Giles was already using Worcester in quantity before 1767. For example, in his *Dictionary of Worcester Porcelain*[6], John Sandon illustrates a tea service painted with Giles fancy birds, which he dates between 1760 and 1765. Secondly, there is the armorial evidence of the well-known dessert service decorated with the arms of Gavin impaling Hearsey, no. 78. David Gavin, the son of a Scottish merchant, married Christina Hearsey in 1751. She died in 1767, and in 1770 David married Elizabeth Maitland, the eldest daughter of the Earl of Lauderdale. Since the impaled arms are those of his first wife, Christina, this service must have been decorated before her death in 1767, and, it seems reasonable to suppose, some time before that event. This shape of plate was introduced by the Worcester Factory in the mid-1760s, which suggests a similar date[7] for this service. This is supported by H R Marshall[8], who in a paper, *Armorial Worcester Porcelain*, given to the English Ceramic Circle in 1943, quotes the view of Algernon Tudor-Craig that both this service and that painted with the arms of Beaumont, no. 79, should be dated 'about 1765 on grounds of

heraldic style'. The Gavin/Hearsey service was an extensive one judging by the number of pieces that have survived, and it consisted not only of the larger, twelve-lobed dessert plates, an example of which is in the exhibition, but also included a number of smaller, scallop-edged plates. In addition a teacup and saucer from a service painted with the Gavin crest, and most probably of about the same date, are in the Marshall Collection[9] in the Ashmolean Museum.

The existence of these three important armorial services and the tea service described above, all certainly Giles decorated on Worcester porcelain, and all pre-dating 1767, indicate that Giles was buying undecorated Worcester tea and dessert services before his advertisement in the same year. It was suggested in Chapter 1 that Giles's advertisement in Mortimer's *The Universal Directory* in 1763 probably reflected some turning point in his career. In terms of timing it might well have been his decision to switch from Chinese to Worcester as his source of undecorated porcelain.

Giles's earliest use of Worcester porcelain may have been the coffee cups and milk jugs of the 'mixed' services, no. 106, or the group of straight-sided and bell-shaped mugs whose main decoration is enclosed within a panel outlined with a red and black line border with barbed corners, a form of decoration not used by Giles on any other Worcester porcelain. Within the panels are either fancy birds on yellow rocks, no. 56, or landscape scenes in green, no. 107. The birds are similar to those found on Giles painted Chinese porcelain, and the landscape scenes are by the same hand as those on the mixed Chinese and Worcester service. One would expect Giles to have tried out some Worcester porcelain before committing his workshop to it exclusively, and these mugs, together with the components of the mixed services, may be evidence of this, probably dating from the early

---

[5] John Sandon, *The Dictionary of Worcester Porcelain*, Vol. 1, page 177.

[6] John Sandon, op. cit., Colour Plate 47, page 176.

[7] For a different view, see Simon Spero & John Sandon, op. cit., page 346, where it is argued that the paste and glaze of this service indicate a date of 1772-73. It is, however, impossible to reconcile such a late date with the fact that the impaled arms are those of Gavin's first wife, who died in 1767.

[8] H R Marshall, *ECC Transactions*, Vol. 2, 1946, page 213. Algernon Tudor-Craig was the author of *Armorial Porcelain of the Eighteenth Century*.

---

[9] Illustrated in H R Marshall, *Coloured Worcester Porcelain of the First Period* 1954. Plate 44, no. 913.

1760s. His work on Bow porcelain is probably of about the same date, and may have been part of the same trial process, although, as we have seen in Chapter 3, it could have been commissioned by the factory.

Giles's flower painting on Chinese porcelain is very much in Meissen style, while his fancy birds and landscape scenes, although ultimately inspired by the German factory, are more immediately derived from Chelsea. In the 1763 advertisement Giles states that he decorates 'in the European or Chinese taste', and in *The Public Advertiser* five years later, he refers again to 'the Dresden, Chelsea and Chinese tastes'. This indicates that during the early years after he had switched to Worcester he continued to decorate in the same 'European' styles as he had on Chinese porcelain. Thus, some of the Worcester dessert and tea services, edged with simple gilt rims and painted with Meissen flowers, in colours, no. 3, or in monochrome, no. 26, fruit, no. 35 or fancy birds, no. 58, probably belong to this 1763-67 period, together with some landscape scenes in green. A few of these services Giles marked with a Chelsea-type brown anchor, no. 47 - something he probably would not have done after the Chelsea factory had gone out of business, which it did in 1768.

Another group of Meissen inspired patterns which probably belong to this period are those featuring naturalistic birds perched on stringy branches. They are found most commonly on tea wares. In some examples, apart from the birds, the only other decoration is the odd flower spray and gilding on the rims. However, there are also two patterns where the birds are in panels reserved against a sea green ground, nos. 72 and 74, and one against an under-glaze blue-scale ground, no. 69. There is also a service which has an irregular yellow border, no. 71. The gilding associated with all these variations is modest in quality, and, in the case of the sea green grounds, in a style unique to these particular patterns. This feature, too, suggests that Giles's naturalistic bird painting predates

the last years of the 1760s when his gilding took on a new and much more opulent quality.

This sea green ground[10] is not found on any other Giles decoration. Its quality is uneven and blotchy, and Giles may have decided that it was not good enough to justify using again. Its presence does, however, show that Giles was experimenting with coloured grounds as a form of decoration, and during the second half of the 1760s the workshop produced a variety of different on-glaze colours. Some of these are very rare, suggesting that like the sea green they were hard to create and not entirely satisfactory in the result.

One of these is a jade green, found only on tea wares and used in conjunction with cloud-shaped reserved panels in which are painted either flower sprays in puce, no. 25, or fancy birds in colours. The ground colour is decorated with rather crude gilt diapering, which again suggests an early date of about 1765. Another rare colour is that now referred to as 'claret', and used as a ground colour on tea services painted either with small fancy birds, no. 62, or with flowers, or as a border on the celebrated Hope-Edwards service, no. 44. This, too, is blotchy and uneven like the greens, but it is invariably accompanied by fine *ciselé* gilding which suggests a slightly later date of perhaps 1767-70.

A more satisfactory green is almost certainly that described as 'pea green' in the 1774 sale catalogue. It is only found on tea wares, both plain, no. 14, and fluted, no. 15, and as a cornucopia border outlined with gilding and in association with flower painting. It is of good and consistent quality, which makes it surprising that it is so rarely used by Giles. Perhaps it was simply not a popular colour with his

_____

[10] Gerald Coke, op. cit. page 36, suggests that this is the 'sea-green' in the list of colours included in the advertisement for Burnsall's 1769 sale, but as discussed in Chapter 1, this sale was almost certainly made up of Factory decorated wares.

contemporary market. Again a date of about 1765-70 is suggested, with the fluted version, which has an under-glaze blue fretted square Factory mark, succeeding the plain.

There are two on-glaze blue colours used by the Giles workshop, one now usually referred to as 'sky blue' and the other, paler, more turquoise, generally called 'bleu céleste' from the Sèvres ground colour which it copied. The first may be dismissed briefly. It appears only on what was probably a single tea service, as a cornucopia border with flower painting , no. 17. Although it is an attractive colour, its quality is poor and it is uneven to the point that it is rough to the touch. Again, it probably made its brief appearance between 1765-70.

The history of the bleu céleste ground is a different story. It must have been introduced at about the same time as Giles's other ground colours, but, unlike them, it continued to be used in a variety of roles throughout the remaining years of the workshop's existence, and there are a number of services described in the 1774 sale catalogue as 'blue céleste'. Moreover, in the advertisement for the May 1770 sale of Giles wares, the stock is described as 'ornamented with Mazarine and Sky Blue and Gold'. In other words, apart from the Factory's under-glaze blue grounds which are here referred to as 'Mazarine' blue, the only colour that has survived is 'sky blue' - the name that Giles used for the colour that the 1774 sale catalogue calls 'bleu céleste'. It may also be significant that this is the ground colour used for the two sample pattern plates, no. 23, and the bowl.[11]

The earliest use of bleu céleste is probably in conjunction with fruit and flowers in cloud shaped panels, no. 42. Like the other colours, the quality of the earliest examples is uneven,

but presumably because it proved popular the workshop persisted with its use, and over time it improved. It appears in a number of different roles, including alternating with a hop trellis in the border of a dessert service, no. 16, and embellished with fine gilding as a cornucopia border on one of Giles's most sumptuous dessert services, no. 43. It was also frequently used as an overall ground on tea and dessert services whose only other decoration is subdued gilding, no. 100, and on these services the colour is invariably even and consistent.

The workshop also used cornucopia-shaped borders made up of coloured scales in imitation of the Meissen 'mosaic' borders of the 1740s. These are all rare, perhaps because they must have been labour intensive to paint and expensive to produce. The most common is made up of pink scales, and is found not only on the usual tea and dessert services, nos. 39 and 40, but also on baskets and large hexagonal vases. Other borders are made up of purple and sea green scales, no. 45, and red and yellow scales, while a particularly striking example is the saxe-blue scale, whose only recorded use is as a border in conjunction with iron red figures, no. 91. Their use was probably confined to the last half of the 1760s. To the same period may belong the so-called 'Atherton' service, whose main decoration is composed of rather crudely painted yellow scales, no. 24.

About 1765 the Worcester Factory introduced its under-glaze blue grounds, including the scale-blue ground which it invented, and which was to become by far the commonest of Giles's ground colours. The ledger shows that Giles continued to buy wares part decorated in this way up to the end of 1774, so that they were used by the workshop throughout the last ten years of its existence. As we saw in the previous chapter, the standard format has thirteen panels when used on flat objects like plates. A later version, almost certainly made at Giles's instigation, has a much simplified configuration of four panels, while another format with nine panels is only

---

[11] The three different panels on the bowl are illustrated in the catalogue of Albert Amor's 1983 Exhibition, the Elegant Porcelain of James Giles, no.1.

found on deep dishes, no. 65. Two reasons why Giles may have favoured the Factory applied blue-scale ground were that the unit cost should have been relatively low, and secondly that it showed off his finest gilding to brilliant effect. He used it principally for tea and dessert services, painted with the traditional flowers, insects and fancy birds in the panels, and with fine *ciselé* gilding on the blue ground. These ingredients are used in two of his most famous and splendid patterns - the Lord Craven pattern, no. 19, and the Lady Mary Wortley Montagu pattern, nos. 64-67, of which there are no less than seven different variations[12]. One of Giles's earliest uses of a scale blue ground is in conjunction with a naturalistic bird pattern, no. 69, and one of the last examples is on a tea service with different urns in the panels, no. 87. The latter bears Factory crescent marks which, when used with on-glaze decoration, confirm that the porcelain cannot have been manufactured earlier than about 1774. The same mark is also found on plates and dishes with an under-glaze, wet blue border, which is always decorated with elaborate gilding.

After the Seven Years' War the Meissen Factory went into decline and Sèvres replaced it as the leading Continental manufacturer. Although he never advertises the fact, from about 1770 Giles stopped decorating 'in the Dresden taste', and his style came to reflect the influence of the French factory. His flower painting, in particular, became more formal and stylised: the flowers are arranged in wreaths or entwined round, and suspended from, gilt or coloured bands, no. 9. As before they are painted in colours or in monochrome, some very fine dry blue flower decoration being a feature of this period , no. 30.

About the same time the revival in classical taste brought about by the excavations at Herculaneum, and expressed in the architecture of Robert Adam, began to influence porcelain design and decoration. One of Giles's responses to this new fashion was the series of services painted with different urns in the centre surrounded by various coloured and floral borders. These date from the last few years of the workshop. From the same period are neo-classical designs in gold like that of the caudle cup and stand, no. 99. Rather surprisingly Giles does not appear to have painted any armorial services during this last phase.

One of the difficulties of dating Giles's decoration is that some patterns clearly continued over a long period. The Lady Mary Wortley Montagu pattern is a case in point. It was probably one of the earliest patterns Giles produced when he first had access to wares part decorated with blue-scale grounds about 1765-67, and the fact that some examples are marked with the Factory crescent, not introduced in this context until 1774, mean that he went on painting it until the end of his career. Similarly the landscape scenes in green first feature on Chinese porcelain of 1755-60 and are still to be found in the 1770s - the purchase of the service at Corsham Court is recorded in the Methuen cash book for 1771, and the 1774 sale catalogue describes lot 28 on the fifth day as 'a complete set of 43 pieces painted with different green landscapes', although the latter could have been painted some years before it came up for sale.

---

[12] Listed by Gerald Coke, op. cit., page 164.

The following is a list of features or mannerisms identified with the Giles workshop. In some cases they may be unique to it - the use of winter jasmine, for instance - while in others Giles puts his own particular stamp on objects which are more commonly used: his 'hairy' gooseberries, for example, and his practice of painting mushrooms in pairs, one with its pleated under-side showing. In terms of distinguishing between Giles and Worcester Factory decoration, it is not only the actual objects like flowers, fruit and insects which may be different, but also the composition of the painting: Giles's has a pleasing freedom and informality together with a brighter palette which is quite unlike the Factory's work, certainly from about 1765 onwards.

1. FLOWERS

Flowers are the workshop's most commonly used decorative feature, and the following dozen are amongst the most distinctive and the most frequently found. It has to be said, however, that Giles's flowers are not always easily identifiable and indeed there is one in the list, which although frequently met, has so far defied identification.

ROSE, pink in colour, the bottom petals are usually wide open, while the top ones are tightly shut and occasionally delicately outlined in black. More rarely a yellow rose, shaded with fawn.	
CONVOLVULUS, often with trailing tendril, the flower usually in blue.	
LILY, the flower a bright orange.	
LILY OF THE VALLEY	
HEARTSEASE, very commonly used both in colour and monochrome.	

TULIP, often with divergent petals, and one of Giles's most celebrated mannerisms. It is derived from Meissen and found in the workshop's finest flower painting.	
IRIS, sometimes with divergent petals.	
WINTER JASMINE, accurately painted in a brilliant yellow, but also in monochrome. This may be unique to Giles. A summer jasmine in pink is also found .	
AURICULA	
FORGET-ME-NOT	
SCARLET PIMPERNEL	
UNIDENTIFIED FLOWER X, possibly a peony.	

2. FRUIT

After flowers, fruit is Giles's most common form of decoration. It is very rarely found in monochrome.

GOOSEBERIES, often quite hairy, and in a variety of colours - yellow, blue and brown.	
APPLES, whole or sliced.	
PEARS, whole or sliced, yellow or deep purple.	
CHERRIES, invariably an iron red colour.	
CURRANTS, black, red and white.	
WILD STRAWBERRIES.	
MULBERRIES or blackberries - sometimes difficult to tell apart.	
PLUMS or damsons in dark or lightish blue.	

ROSE HIPS.	
PEACHES.	
GRAPES.	

3. VEGETABLES

MUSHROOMS, often in pairs with one showing its pleated underside.	

4. GILDING

Almost all Giles decorated wares have gilt rims.

DENTIL EDGE.	
DOTS of diminishing size running down backs of handles, often accompanied by gilding on the sides.	
GILT bands around foot rims, covering the whole rim on richer services	

COLOURED GROUNDS and most borders are outlined in gilt.	
CHEVRONS or bars of diminishing in size and becoming dots down backs of handles.	
BIRDS EYE and sprig borders inside rims.	
GRUBBE plate 1 type border on rims.	
CISELE gilding on coloured grounds, i.e. gilding which has been tooled and burnished into decorative designs.	

5. INSECTS

BUTTERFLIES in fantastic colours with unnaturally long thin wings, and curiously folded legs overlapping antennae.	
BEETLES and various other types of insect.	

6. ASSOCIATED WITH BIRD DECORATION

YELLOW ROCKS or ground with brown edges, likened to a piece of cheese, on which many fancy birds stand.	
STRINGY BRANCHES on which naturalistic birds are generally perched.	

7. BORDERS

CORNUCOPIA-shaped borders of different colours outlined in gilt.	
CONCENTRIC narrow blue bands with regular gilt bars, in pairs.	
BROWN band interwoven with green foliage.	
NARROW BANDS embellished with trailing flowers, usually gilt but sometimes monochrome when used with monochrome flowers.	

8. MISCELLANEOUS

COFFEE CUPS - painting inside: Giles almost invariably paints a small flower spray or some other decorative device in the bottom of coffee cups, the Factory never does except in the case of some oriental patterns.	
FLORETS on the intersections of baskets are generally painted on in blue with red centres.	

Although the work of the Giles atelier on glass is clearly of secondary importance in terms of output and general interest, it is of great significance to the few for whom glass takes precedence over porcelain.

It is surprising to learn that it was as recently as 1959 that the late R. J. Charleston, then Keeper of the Department of Ceramics at the Victoria and Albert Museum, first focussed on Giles's work on glass. He noted motifs carried out in gold alone on a small number of porcelains unarguably decorated by Giles, which could also be found on glass, principally, but not exclusively, on enamel (or opaque-white) glass. This connection demonstrated, there seemed little prospect of following the matter further. But in 1966, Charleston's attention was drawn to the now well-known Catalogue of Giles's stock sold by Christie's in 1774 and still retained in their archive. (See Chapter 1). A study of the descriptions of the articles offered, which were reasonably detailed, reveals that there were some 50 or so items of glass, again principally, if not exclusively, opaque-white.

Perhaps the most frequently encountered forms of gilding on glass attributed to the studio would include flowers, insects, exotic birds etc., the latter striding a groundwork which includes recognisable traits such as heart-shaped leaves. Some of the sprigs of flowers appear also on porcelain, achieved by the same artist, no. 124. What other features provide links between glass and china? There are at least two: The Grubbe plate No. 1, Figure 1, with landscape in green monochrome, has a complex border of gold trellis. It is noted again on the coffee pot displayed here, no. 111. This border is frequently seen on glass, usually in association with flowers, no. 124. Secondly, one of the patterns detailed in the Christie's sale, described there as "stags heads, pateras, festoons, etc.", now known as the Bucrania pattern, turns up on

Worcester porcelain as well as on opaque-white glass, no. 127.

An interesting aspect of the Studio's decorations on glass is that it falls so very clearly into two fields: rococo and neo-classical. Most of the former is carried out on coloured and colourless glass; most of the latter appears on opaque-white, or is engraved on colourless glass. It is clear that the Studio employed many painters. Yet, with glass, it seems that virtually all of the decorations prior to Giles embracing neo-classicism are by the same hand. The striding birds, their groundwork and flanking trees and all the flower decorations are readily attributable to this one unknown artist, nos. 124 and 129. Figure subjects are rare, but the oeuvre includes a series of garden statues and bizarre architectural inventions – eccentric buildings standing on bridges etc, no. 125, which are surely unique to his glass decorations.

There is frequent use of what is described in the 1774 catalogue as "mosaics". These formal patterns appear on cut surfaces and comprise a narrow repertoire of sunbursts, circumferential dots together with, in the angles of facets, invariable arrow-heads, no. 128. These diapers appear to represent the only transition between the two styles: they appear in association with both. They are rarely seen on porcelain, the gilding on the spout of the coffee pot, no. 111, being an example.

Gilding on all the earlier, rococo pieces, and, to a less extent, the later neo-classical pieces was enhanced by "scratching out" with a sharp steel point. This technique allowed considerable detail to be added to an otherwise flat gold silhouette; detail such as anthers for flowers, veins for leaves, shading for grapes and so forth. It could be said that the technique is the equivalent on glass of refined *ciselé* gilding on porcelain.

As to the gilding itself, it seems clear that, in relation to glass, the temperature required to fix the gold was high. This is a relative and inexact term, of course, but all know that it was the last firing of decorated porcelain at the lowest temperature of all previous firings which fixed the gold. It is normal to find the undersides of Giles items of gilded glass to be pitted and distorted by the heat of the floor of the kiln. For example, it is possible to see how the stopper of the decanter, no. 129 lay in the kiln. One would expect it to have been placed upright, but, if it was, it must have fallen over; one facet is pitted. Incidentally, the decanter itself has a pronounced lean; doubtless also the effect of excessive heat.

It is curious that Giles's headlong entry into the fashionable world of neo-classicism occurs so clearly in glass yet hardly at all in porcelain. We have seen patterns of the 1770s centred by sketchy vases wreathed in flowers, no. 84, but they do not form a particularly significant proportion of the Studio's extensive output. Suddenly, Giles, like Duesbury at Derby, re-discovered a whole new vocabulary. The source for much of this new style for Giles as for others is soon identified. Sir William Hamilton returned from Diplomatic posting at Naples with three collections of classic Greek vases. One group he sold to the new British Museum, another vanished beneath the waves off Scilly, the third he presumably kept. To disseminate his then personal interest in this collecting field, he commissioned Baron Pierre-Francois Hugues d'Hancarville to produce a book of engravings to record the collections. The four volumes were completed between 1766 and 1776[1] and were highly influential in putting before the public the "Antique Taste". See Fig. 11, an opaque-white beaker described in Christie's catalogue of 1774 as "….cut in flutes, painted work, with Tuscan and Grecian figures from Hamilton". They contributed a rich ingredient to

the "Vase Madness" mentioned in Catalogue VI. A glance at nos.125 and 127 shows what changes a year or two wrought in the glass products of the Giles workshop.

Giles's account books reveal his close association with William Parker and, to a lesser extent Stephen Hall of the Falcon glasshouse, Southwark. It is probable that Parker, who bought his glass from the Whitefriars glasshouse, will have made most of Giles's glass, although he may have bought blue from Hall. Engraved editions of the Bucrania pattern exist in colourless glass, the cut areas of which match those on some of the opaque-white decanters listed in the Christie's catalogue. Doubtless these too were produced in Parker's workshops. Engraved examples include decanters, finger bowls (wash-hand cups); wineglasses are also seen *en suite*.

Finally there is the series of coloured cut glass scent bottles decorated in vitreous enamel in high relief with gilded detail, Fig. 6. Normally they are cut in hollow diamonds and appear in blue, green, amethyst, colourless and opaque-white. They have always evaded attribution. Yet those gilded with rich mosaics have always been accepted as Giles. The latter are frequently finished on the shoulder with gold arrowheads arranged radially about the neck with its gold cap. Identical treatment is accorded many of the enamelled versions. Whoever decorated the one type, decorated the other. After all, the bottles themselves were, or could be, identical, doubtless from the same source; and the Giles Studio was perfectly capable of dealing both with the enamelling and with the gilding. One should not forget the dots of vitreous enamel often applied to the intersections of the patterns of the mosaic bottles, acceptably Giles.

From study of the pieces here, it can surely be agreed that the glass decorated in gold by the Giles atelier forms a group both beautiful and technically brilliant. It neatly illustrates in this narrow field the move from rococo to neo-classical style between 1765 and 1775.

---

[1] *Antiquites Etrusques, Grecques et Romaines Tirees du Cabinet de M Hamilton*
(First edition Naples 1766-7)

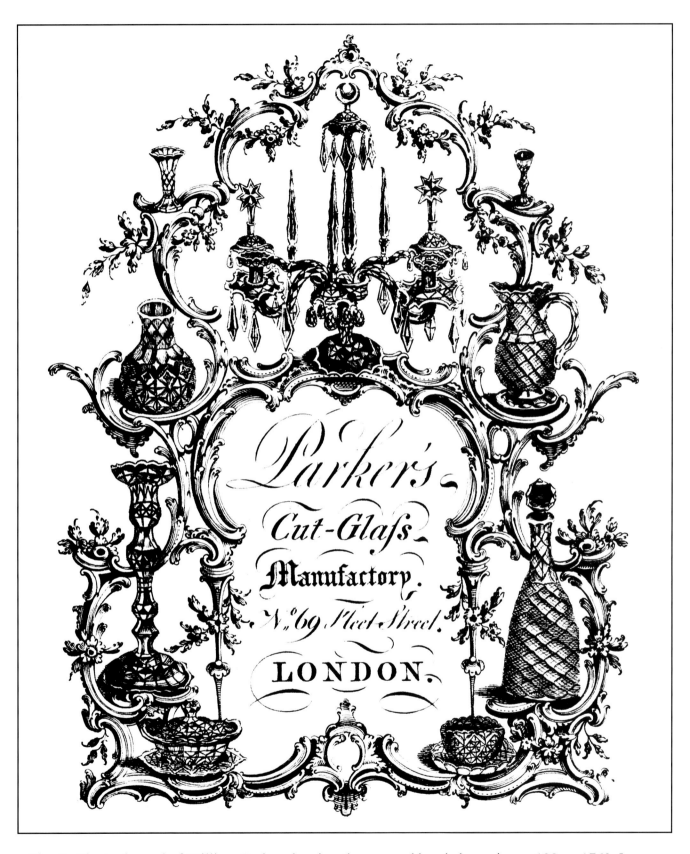

Fig. 3. The trade card of William Parker showing the covered bowl shown in no. 128. c. 1762-5

CATALOGUE

FLOWER DECORATION

Flowers were by far the commonest form of decoration used by the Giles workshop and they were employed in a number of different ways - on their own, mixed with different types of fruits, as borders, and as scattered sprays or sprigs supplementing some other form of decoration. They are found in reserved panels, and as wreaths round urns. They are more often in polychrome, but they also appear in single colours - 'dry' blue, carmine, purple or two shades of green. Of the pieces in this exhibition, about a quarter have flowers as their main decoration, and about three quarters include flower decoration of some sort. Because they are so common, they are often the most important evidence in attributing a piece of decoration to the Giles workshop.

Giles's earlier flower painting was strongly influenced by the style of the Meissen factory, initially and for many years the market leader among the European manufacturers. A typical composition was made up of one large bouquet of different flowers, often placed on the right hand side of a plate or a saucer, with other sprays of single flower types, scattered informally over the rest of the surface, nos. 1, 3, and 5. Later, as a result of the disruption caused by The Seven Years' War (1756-63), Meissen went into decline, and from about 1765 Sèvres established itself as the leading Continental manufacturer. Giles style came under the influence of the French factory, and his flower painting tends to become more formal and symmetrical: flowers are suspended from gilt or coloured bands or arranged in trailing festoons, nos. 6, 9, and 30.

Giles's workshop was in production for more than thirty years, during which it grew from a small enterprise employing a handful of staff to a substantial business which must have had a large payroll. Over this period there would have been a considerable recruitment and turnover of workers specialising in flower painting. Moreover, while for the first twenty years or so Giles was probably running the workshop himself, and personally carrying out some of the painting, from 1767 when he opened his own retail showroom, he must have increasingly delegated the day-to-day management of the decorating business to somebody else. Despite these factors, and the parallel development away from the less structured style of Meissen to the more formal one of Sèvres, the workshop's flower painting remained surprisingly distinctive and consistent. A number of different hands or sub-styles are clearly discernable, but at the same time Giles was able to maintain a recognisable house style, and, as a result, his flower painting is on the whole readily distinguishable from that of the Worcester Factory. This is a result partly of the individual flower types he used, partly of the more informal, sometimes random way in which he disposed them, and partly of the different and brighter palette he employed. We have no idea how the workshop was managed and organised to achieve this, but one might envisage a number of different foremen, each with his own personal style, and each with a group of hands or apprentices under him, trained to copy it. This would explain why services exist in which the quality of the painting varies from piece to piece, no. 9, and why one finds similar variations of quality in identical groupings of flowers in different patterns, nos. 19 and 65.

A list of the flower types more commonly used by the workshop is included in Chapter 5. It should be noted that while Giles's craftsmen generally painted the actual flowers with reasonable accuracy, the associated leaves often bear little or no resemblance to the real ones.

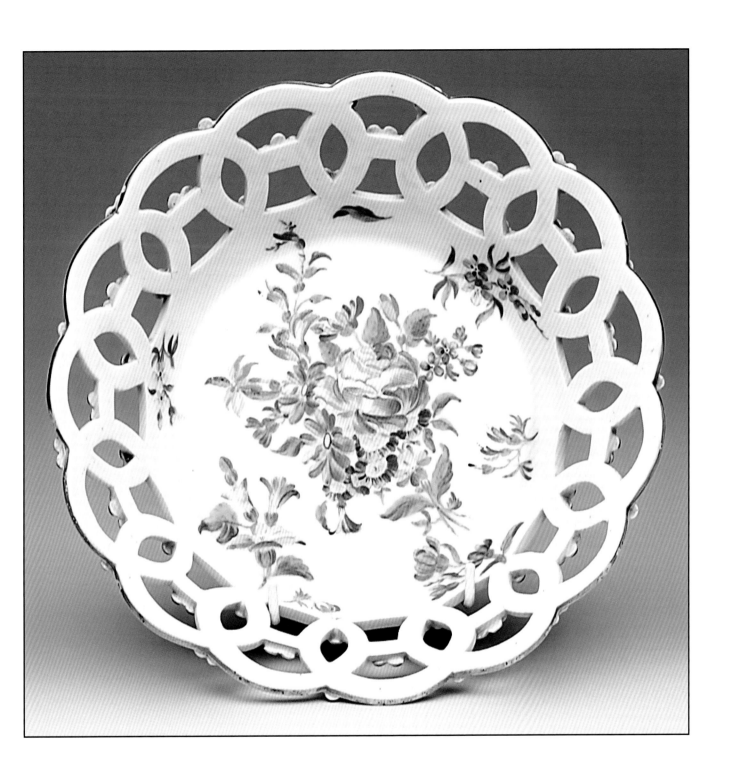

Basket, no. 2.

Throughout this catalogue all items are Worcester porcelain unless otherwise stated.

1(a) Flowers in Colours

1. A Saucer,
of Chinese porcelain, with a brown rim, painted with a large bouquet of mixed flowers and scattered flower sprays and two insects.
c.1755-60.
Diameter: 12.7 cm   Mark: none.

Provenance: the Hartley Asquith Collection.

The flower painting on this saucer is similar to that on the pair of Chinese plates, no. 75.
Giles features: pink rose, convolvulus, heartsease, tulip with divergent petals, flower x.

2. A Basket,
painted in colours with a bouquet of flowers surrounded by scattered sprays.
c.1763-68.
Diameter: 24.1 cm.   Mark: none.

This basket is painted in a style sometimes known as that of 'the wind-blown flower painter'.
Giles features: pink rose, auriculas, red and blue florets at intersections.

3. A Pair of Plates,
painted in colours with a large spray of flowers on the right hand side and scattered sprays of flowers elsewhere.
c.1763-68.
Diameter: 21 cm.   Mark: none.

Giles features: pink roses, convolvulus, tulip with divergent petals.

4. A Basket,
of oval shape painted with sprays of flowers in the base and smaller flowers irregularly scattered around the pierced sides.
c. 1765-70.
Length: 29.2 cm.   Mark: none.

Giles features: pink rose, yellow rose, iris with divergent petals, lilies, red and blue florets at intersections.

5. A Stand,
of circular shape painted in colours with one large spray of flowers and scattered single flowers.
c.1763-68.
Diameter: 16 cm.   Mark: none.
Provenance: the Dr H J Elverson Collection.

The painting on this stand is similar to that on the basket, no.2, in the style of 'the wind blown flower painter'.
Giles features: lily.

1   4   5

3   2   3

6. A Milk Jug,

painted with swirling swags of European flowers with an occasional insect between.
c. 1768-73.
Height: 10.9 cm.   Mark: none.

This pattern, which was inspired by Sèvres, is also used by Giles in conjunction with a pink scale border.
Giles features: gilt band round the foot rim, dots of diminishing size down the back of the handle.

7. A Plate,

moulded with sprays of rose leaves and buds growing from a common stalk, all painted in natural colours. In between there are a spray of flowers and different individual flowers painted in colours.
The Blind Earl pattern.
c.1765-70.
Diameter: 19 cm.   Mark: none.

These moulded plates were first made by the Worcester Factory in about 1760. They were made in two sizes of which this is the larger. Factory decorated examples are relatively common, and the rose leaves are invariably painted a darker green than those decorated in the Giles workshop, which are rarer, especially those painted with flowers rather than insects. They are named after the Earl of Coventry who was blinded in a hunting accident.
Giles features: pink rose, convolvulus, heartsease.

8. A Teacup and Saucer, and a Can,

painted in colours with a bouquet of European flowers and scattered sprays.
c. 1763-68.
Diameter of saucer: 12.9 cm, height of cup: 4.5 cm, height of can: 6.1 cm.
Marks: the cup and saucer have crossed swords and *9* with dot in under-glaze blue, the can is unmarked.
Provenance: the Anthony Wood Collection, the cup and saucer previously in the Gerald Coke Collection.
Exhibited: the Albert Amor 1983 Exhibition, *The Elegant Porcelain of James Giles*, no. 71

This is one of Giles's rare repeating patterns where the decoration on each piece of the service is more or less identical. It is not clear whether the can was originally part of the service and an early example of the use of a can for coffee, or whether it was simply a small mug of the same pattern.
For similar unusual Giles flower painting, see the reserved panels on a blue ground plate illustrated in Coke, *In Search of James Giles*, no. 37 (a).
Giles features: pink rose, flower x.

9. A Plate,

round the border is a wreath of flowers in colour with a broad gold line running through it, with further sprays of flowers suspended from it towards the centre.
c.1768-73.
Diameter: 22.7 cm.   Mark: none.

This plate, from a service of some 20 pieces, was exhibited by Robyn Robb at the 2004 International Ceramics Fair in London. It included shaped dishes, and about a dozen plates. The painting, while good, varied considerably, suggesting a number of different hands were responsible for the one service.
Giles features: pink roses, auriculas, convolvulus, rosehips.

8   6

7   9

10. A Basket, Cover and Stand,

of oval shape, with pierced cover and stand, rustic handles with encrusted flower sprays, the centre of the stand is painted with scattered flowers in colours.

c. 1765-70.

Length of stand: 25.3 cm, height complete: 17.7 cm.   Mark: none.

Giles features: pink rose, convolvulus, red and blue florets on cover and sides of basket.

11. A Teacup and Saucer,

painted with flowers and a chocolate-brown band entwined with a continuous garland of leaves round the outside of the cup and the rim of the saucer.

c.1768-73.

Diam. of saucer: 12.7 cm, height of cup: 5 cm.   Mark: crossed swords and *9* in under-glaze blue on cup.

This pattern is also found on dessert services (no. 12) and the border was used in conjunction with urn-decoration (no. 86). Inside the base of the cup there is an orange peony, and it is unusual for Giles to place the principal decoration in this way.

Giles features: pink rose, tulip with divergent petals, gilt band round foot rim, gilding on sides of handle, chocolate brown band interwoven with green foliage.

12. A Dish,

of lozenge shape, in the base there is a large bouquet of flowers painted in colours.

c.1768-73.

Width: 29 cm.   Mark: none.

Giles features: convolvulus, chocolate brown band interwoven with green foliage.

13. A Plate,

around the centre and around the rim are two pairs of narrow concentric blue lines with pairs of gilt bars at intervals. In the centre is a bouquet of flowers in colours and there are four sprays of flowers, symmetrically placed, between the sets of blue rings.

c. 1768-73.

Diameter: 21 cm.   Mark: none.

The double blue line borders are copied from Sèvres.

Giles features: pink rose, lily, scarlet pimpernel, double blue line border.

10

12   11   13

I (b) Flower Decoration with Coloured Grounds and Borders

14. A Sugar Bowl and Cover,
painted in colours with European flowers below an irregular apple green border.
c. 1763-68.
Height: 13 cm.   Mark: none.

The Giles green ground is paler than that used at the Worcester Factory, and is relatively rare, being confined to tea wares. The colour was derived from Sèvres, where it was introduced in 1756, and where it was often overlaid with gilding. At both the Worcester Factory and the Giles workshop, however, the gilding invariably outlined the green ground and never overlapped it. See also no. 15.
Giles features: pink rose, yellow rose, forget-me-nots, tulip with divergent petals, cornucopia border outlined with gilding.

15. A Teacup, Coffee Cup and Saucer,
of fluted form, painted in colours with flowers below an irregular apple green border. Inside the base of each cup there is a single flower spray.
c. 1765-68.
Diameter of saucer: 14 cm, height of coffee cup: 6 cm, height of teacup: 5 cm.
Marks: a fretted square in under-glaze blue.

The teacup appears to have been painted by a different hand from the coffee cup and the saucer.
Lot 60 on the last day of Christie's sale of Giles stock in March 1774 is described in the catalogue as 'a compleat set of tea china fluted and pea green border…. 39 pieces', which possibly relates to this trio.
See also no. 14.
Giles features: pink rose, forget-me-nots, heartsease, dots of diminishing size down handles, cornucopia border outlined with gilding, flower in bottom of coffee cup.

16. A Dish,
of deep, square shape with an irregular fluted rim, the border has eight *bleu céleste* panels, alternating with eight panels of puce trellis tied with three gilt lines. In the centre there is a bouquet of flowers and eight sprays of individual flowers.
c. 1768-73.
Width: 21.6 cm.   Mark: none.

This pattern, derived from Sèvres, is also found on two-handled chocolate cups and stands, but not on tea services.
Giles features: pink rose, tulip with divergent petals, lily, scarlet pimpernel.

17. A Teacup and Saucer,
painted in colours with flowers below an irregular, sky-blue border outlined with gilt scrolling.
c. 1765-68.
Diameter of saucer: 13.3 cm, height of cup: 4.5 cm.
Marks: crossed swords and '*9*' with dot in under- glaze blue.

The blue has less green than the more common *bleu céleste*, and has a rough surface. This appears to be the only service decorated in this colour.

14

15

16

17

Giles features: pink rose, tulip with divergent petals, convolvulus, dots of diminishing size down the backs of handles, cornucopia border outlined with gilding.

18. A Plate,
with panels reserved against a blue-scale ground and decorated with sprays of flowers and single flowers.
c. 1768-73.
Diameter: 20.3 cm.   Mark: a fretted square in under-glaze blue.

This pattern differs from the Lord Craven pattern, no. 19, by virtue of its paler palette and less elaborate gilding.
Giles features: pink rose, lily of the valley, heartsease, iris, ciselé gilding.

19. A Plate,
with panels reserved against a blue-scale ground and decorated with sprays of flowers and single flowers.
The Lord Craven Service.
c.1768-73.
Diameter: 22.5 cm.   Mark: a fretted square in under-glaze blue.

The 6th Baron Craven was born in 1738 and died in 1791. His name appears in Giles's ledger, and from December 1771 to January 1772 he bought four parcels of china to the considerable value of £86:7:6. There is, however, no description of the services he bought, and it is not clear how his name became associated with this pattern.
The flower types and grouping in the right hand panel are also found in a panel on the dish, no. 65, suggesting that both may have been copied from a common pattern.
Giles features: pink rose, auriculas, tulip with divergent petals, forget-me-nots, lily of the valley, convolvulus with trailing tendril, scarlet pimpernel, ciselé gilding.

20. A Custard Cup and Cover,
decorated with panels reserved against a blue-scale ground, outlined with gilding and painted with flowers in colours.
c.1773-76.
Height: 7.1 cm.   Mark: a crescent in under-glaze blue.

Worcester custard cups were made in two shapes: this, the later version, is straight-sided, while the earlier one is ogee shape. The catalogue of the Christie's 1774 sale of Giles stock mentions 'ice cup', which possibly refers to this form .
Compared with the *ciselé* gilding on the Lord Craven plate for example, no. 19, the gilding on this piece is restrained and more like Worcester Factory gilding. It may be that it was considered that the more flamboyant style of gilding that Giles generally used in conjunction with a blue scale-ground would be overwhelming on so small an object.
Giles features: pink rose, lily of the valley, forget-me-nots, gilding on the sides of the handle, dots of diminishing size down the back.

18   19

20   21

21. A Spoon Tray,
decorated with panels reserved against an under-glaze blue ground, outlined with gilding and painted with European flowers in colours.
c. 1768-73.
Width: 16.3 cm.   Marks: a fretted square in under-glaze blue.

Like the custard cup and cover, no. 20, the gilding on this service is restrained and more like Worcester Factory gilding.
Giles features: pink rose, tulip with divergent petals, lilies.

I (c) Flowers only in Monochrome.

22. A Butter Tub, Cover and Stand,
of circular, cylindrical form with lug handles, painted with sprays and sprigs of flowers, outlined and highlighted in black and washed over in two shades of green.
c. 1765-70.
Diameter of stand: 16.1 cm, height of tub with cover: 7 cm.   Marks: none.

Giles features: convolvulus with trailing tendril, iris, heartsease, flower x, auriculas, scarlet pimpernel, lily, gilt dots of diminishing size on the tub's lugs.

23. A Plate,
decorated with a solid turquoise ground reserving four differing panels, painted with swags of green monochrome flowers, fruit and fancy birds, Sèvres style flowers, and the gilt Queen's pattern.
The so-called 'Harlequin' service.
c. 1768-73.
Diameter: 21cm.   Mark: a gold anchor.
Lent by: The Ashmolean Museum, Oxford; (Marshall Gift through the National Art Collections Fund, 1957).
Literature: illustrated in Dinah Reynolds, *Worcester Porcelain in the Ashmolean Museum*, plate 33.

Two of these plates with turquoise ground and different patterns in the reserved panels are known. The second is in the British Museum. They were considered to be travellers' sample plates, until a bowl with similar decoration (now in the Museum of Worcester Porcelain) appeared on the market in the 1970's, and the view was then taken that there must have been a service of this pattern. However, a bowl of slop basin size is not normally part of a desert service, and all three pieces may well have been sample wares, showing different patterns available from the workshop.
Giles features: double blue line border, rose, auriculas, tulip with divergent petal in right hand panel, the bird pecking fruit, similar to those on no. 62, in the top panel.

24. A Saucer Dish,
of fluted form, painted with a border of bright yellow overlapping scales, from which extend alternately long and short puce foliate garlands.
The Atherton Service.
c. 1765-68.
Diameter: 18.4 cm.   Mark: a fretted square in under-glaze blue.
Provenance: the Zorensky Collection.

22   24

23   Courtesy of the Ashmolean Museum

Literature: illustrated in Bonhams' catalogue of Part I of the sale of the Zorensky Collection, lot 237.

A peculiarity of this service is that all the components are fluted except the coffee cups which are plain.
Giles features: this dish displays no obvious Giles features, but the puce garlands are similar to the green ones found on the border of the plate, no. 73.

25. A Teacup and Saucer,
decorated with quatre-foil panels painted with sprays of different flowers in purple monochrome, reserved against a jade green ground diapered with gilding.
c. 1763-68.
Diameter of saucer: 12.7 cm, height of cup: 5.1 cm.
Mark: crossed swords and *9* with dot in under-glaze blue.

A cup and saucer of this pattern are illustrated in the catalogue of the Drane Collection, no. 865, where it is described as 'a repellant example of an imitation of some Dresden original'.
This is a rare repeating pattern and probably only one service was made. No coffee cups are recorded. Another service has the same green ground and gilding, but fancy birds in the reserved panels. The quality of the gilding, similar to that on some of the naturalistic bird services, suggests a date of 1763-68.
Giles features: lily of the valley, forget-me-not.

26. A Saucer,
with fluted, scalloped, purple rim, painted in purple with a large spray of flowers and scattered sprigs.
c. 1765-70.
Diameter: 11.4 cm.   Mark: a fretted square in under-glaze blue.
Provenance: the Anthony Wood Collection.

Giles features: convolvulus with trailing tendril, winter jasmine.

27. A Teapot Stand,
hexagonal, with a fluted gilt edge, painted with a spray and sprigs of flowers in purple monochrome.
c. 1763-68.
Diameter: 14.4 cm.   Mark: none.
Provenance: the Anthony Wood and Gerald Coke Collections.
Literature: illustrated in Gerald Coke, op. cit., plate 9 (b).

The teapot from this service is in the H R Marshall Collection, and illustrated in Marshall, *Coloured Worcester Porcelain of the First Period*, plate 11, no. 205.
Giles features: lily of the valley, flower x.

28. A Teacup and Saucer,
of fluted form, decorated with panels containing hop wreaths divided by three vertical royal blue poles tied by six gilt bands. In the centre of the saucer and the bottom of the cup there are puce flower sprigs.
c. 1768-73.
Diameter of saucer: 13.6 cm, height of cup: 4.8 cm.   Marks: a fretted square in under-glaze blue.
Provenance: the Anthony Wood Collection.

Giles features: heartsease, gilding on the sides of the cup handle, dots of diminishing size down the back.

25   28

26   27

29. A Coffee Cup,
painted in crimson pink monochrome with a bouquet of flowers and floral sprays.
c. 1763-68.
Height: 6.3 cm.   Mark: none.
Provenance: the Anthony Wood Collection.
Literature: illustrated in the Albert Amor 1980 exhibition catalogue, *The Golden Age, Masterpieces of 18th Century English Porcelain,* no. 64, where it is described as 'probably an early example of the work of James Giles's London workshop'.

30. A Chocolate Cup, Cover and Stand,
painted in over-glaze, mid-blue with floral sprays suspended from a blue line. There is a flower spray inside the bottom of the cup.
c. 1768-73.
Diameter of stand:14 cm, height (including cover) : 12.6 cm, width (including handles): 13 cm.
Marks: none.
Provenance: the stand lent by the Museum of Worcester Porcelain, Worcester.
Literature: the stand is illustrated in Coke, op. cit., plate 8 (a).

This cup and cover with the matching saucer at Worcester appear to be the only examples recorded in this pattern. The same dry blue decoration is also found in one of the panels on the bowl from the so-called 'Harlequin' service, also at Worcester.
Although they are generally referred to as 'chocolate cups', the contemporary name for these objects appears to have been 'caudle cup'. A number were sold in the 1774 sale, usually in pairs, but also in sixes. Lot 71 on the fourth day of the sale was described as 'a pair of caudle cups, covers and stands with fine enamel's blue wreath of flowers', which could refer to this particular cup.
The London Chronicle, 29th August 1765 reported, "The resort of different ranks of the people of St James's to receive the Queen's Caudle is now very great".
Giles features: gilded band round the foot rim, gilding on the sides of the handles, dots of diminishing size down the backs. The use of the band and the flower painting are very similar in style to the polychrome example, no.9.

31. A Bowl,
painted in dry blue with a large bouquet of flowers and smaller sprays.
c. 1763-68.
Diameter: 15.3 cm.   Mark: none.

The flower painting on this bowl is also in the style of 'the wind blown flower painter'. The basket, no. 2, and the stand, no. 5, are examples of the same style in polychrome.
This bowl is the same size as a standard Worcester slop basin, and may originally have been part of a tea service.
Giles features: iris, lilies and heartsease.

31a. A Teacup and Saucer
painted in overglaze mid-blue with sprays of flowers beneath a blue line intertwined with a vine in ciselé gilding. There is a daisy in the bottom of the cup, matching that on the saucer.
c. 1768-73
Diameter of saucer: 13 cm   Mark: crossed swords and *9* with dot in under-glaze blue.

29   31

30   31A

The teapot of this service is in the Powerhouse Museum, Sydney. The pattern of gilding on this service is unusual.

Giles features: gilded band round the foot rim, gilt dentil rim, ciselé gilding, dots of diminishing size on handle.

32. A Teabowl,

of Philip Christian's Liverpool porcelain painted with sprays of flowers in over-glaze dry-blue. There is a narrow gilt band just inside the rim.

c.1771-75.

Diameter: 7.8 cm, height: 3.8 cm.   Mark: none.

Provenance: the Anthony Wood and Dr Bernard Watney Collections.

Literature: this tea bowl is attributed to the Giles workshop by Dr Watney in a paper given to the English Ceramic Circle on 17th November 1990, and is illustrated in the ECC Transactions, Vol. 14, part 3, page 249. It is also illustrated in Dr Watney's *Liverpool Porcelain of the Eighteenth Century,* page 46, and in colour on plate 13c.

In Giles's ledger the purchase of 'a parcel of white China' from Mr Philip Christian & Son is recorded in August 1771.

Giles features: winter jasmine.

33. A Spoon Tray,

of Philip Christian's Liverpool porcelain, with a gilt rim and painted in over-glaze dry-blue with a spray and sprigs of flowers.

c. 1771-75.

Width: 14 cm.   Mark: none.

Another example in dry blue in the style of 'the wind blown flower painter', similar to the bowl, no.31, above.

In Giles's ledger the purchase of 'a parcel of white China' from Mr Philip Christian & Son is recorded in August 1771.

34. A Teabowl and Saucer,

with brown rim, painted with a large flower spray in mauve and three smaller sprays in grey-blue.

c.1763-68.

Diameter of saucer: 12 cm, height of bowl: 4.1 cm.   Mark: none.

Lent by: The Ashmolean Museum, Oxford; (Marshall Gift through the National Art Collections Fund, 1957)

Literature: illustrated in Marshall, op. cit. Plate 11, no.204.

This is a rare repeating pattern and it is likely that only one service was made. No coffee cups are recorded. The large flower spray is similar to that on the back of the 'Golden Fleece' teapot, no. 82.

32   33

34   Courtesy of the Ashmolean Museum, Oxford

After flowers, fruit is the commonest form of decoration used by the Giles workshop. It is very often found in conjunction with flowers, either grouped with them in the same bouquet, as in nos. 35 and 37, or forming the main decoration with a border of different flower sprays, no. 36. Fruit and flowers are also sometimes accompanied by scale borders and coloured grounds - nos. 39, 40, 41 and 45. When fruit is not accompanied by flowers, Giles often adds insects - butterflies and various unidentifiable types of beetles and flies. Different fruits also decorate the border of a well known fancy bird service, no. 57 and bunches of fruit are found in the centre of plates and dishes in another service where fancy birds, either in pairs or singly, are placed on the rims, no. 59. Unlike flower decoration fruits are almost invariably painted in colours, and only very rarely in monochrome - an example of the latter is the so-called 'Horner of Mells' service which has fruit and flowers painted in two shades of green.

As in the case of so much of Giles's decoration, the ultimate source of the workshop's fruit painting was Meissen, but, again, the influence was probably not direct, but via the early gold anchor period of the Chelsea Factory. Indeed some of Giles's services are marked with a brown or a red anchor, no. 47 which would suggest that they were closely copied from Chelsea prototypes. Giles's practice of slicing some of his fruit - particularly apples and pears - is also a mannerism copied from Meissen.

Grubbe plate 3 is an example of Giles's use of fruit in conjunction with flowers, and although its particular scale border is not otherwise recorded, two of Giles's most famous and sumptuous services have very similar decoration. The examples in the exhibition are nos. 43 and 44, a plate with a *bleu céleste* cornucopia border, and a lozenge shaped dish with a similarly shaped claret border. Each has fruit and flower decoration of the highest quality and superb *ciselé* gilding on the coloured border.

Examples of the fruits and insects commonly used by the workshop are listed and illustrated in Chapter 5.

Teapot, no. 39.

II (a) Fruit Decoration with Flowers

35. A Saucer Dish,
painted in colours with a large group of fruit and flowers, and two other sprays of fruit.
c.1763-68.
Diameter: 17.5 cm   Mark: crossed swords and *9* with dot in under-glaze blue.

Giles features: scarlet pimpernel, flower x, sliced and whole apples, gooseberries.

36. A Dish,
with fluted border, in the centre there is a group of fruits painted in colours and around the rim are sprays
of flowers.
c.1763-68.
Diameter: 25.4 cm   Mark: none.

*Giles features: pink rose, yellow rose, lilies, scarlet pimpernel, sliced apple, blackberries, plum,
damsons.*

37. A Plate,
painted in colours with a large bouquet of flowers and a sliced apple. On the rim there are other fruit and
flowers and a mushroom.
c.1763-68.
Diameter: 22.2 cm   Mark: none.
Provenance: the Dr H J Elverson Collection.

*Giles features: tulip with divergent petals, convolvulus, forget-me-nots, auriculas, sliced apple,
gooseberries, and mushroom.*

38. A Teacup and Saucer,
painted with flowers, fruit and a mushroom.
c.1763-68.
Diameter of saucer: 12.7 cm, height of cup: 4.5 cm
Mark: crossed swords, *9*, and a dot in under-glaze blue.
Provenance: Dr & Mrs Sinclair-Gillies Collection, Sydney.

*Giles features: tulip with divergent petal, forget-me-nots, sliced pear, gooseberries, cherries, rosehips,
mushroom, gilding on sides of handle.*

39. A Teapot and Cover,
of globular shape, decorated with irregular pink scale borders, below which are sprays of fruit and
flowers and a pair of mushrooms in colour.
c. 1765-68.
Height: 15 cm.   Mark: crossed swords and *9* with dot in under-glaze blue.

Pink scale grounds were first used by Meissen in the 1750's, and introduced by Giles between 1765-70,
in the form of borders for tea and dessert services, baskets and hexagonal vases. The fish scales are large
and made up of two shades of pink.

35   38   36

37   39

Giles features: yellow rose, auriculas, forget-me-nots, mushrooms, yellow and deep purple pears, cherries, rosehips, cornucopia border outlined with gilding, gilt band round the foot rim, gilt chevrons becoming bands of diminishing size on the handle, gilding on sides of handle.

40. A Bowl,
painted with fruit and flowers in colour beneath an irregular pink scale border.
c. 1765-68.
Diameter: 16.5 cm.   Mark: crossed swords and *9* with dot in under-glaze blue.

From the same service as no. 39.

Giles features: heartsease, rosehips, cornucopia border outlined with gilding, gilt band on the foot rim.

41. A Saucer,
decorated with a *bleu celeste*, cornucopia border, with a spray of fruit and flowers in the centre, and scattered fruit and flowers.
c. 1765-70.
Diameter: 12.7 cm.   Mark: crossed swords, *9*, and a dot in under-glaze blue.
Provenance: the Anthony Wood Collection.

This appears to be an otherwise unrecorded pattern. This turquoise or *bleu celeste* ground colour was first used at Vincennes in 1753, and was much favoured by Giles.
Giles features: tulip with divergent petals, scarlet pimpernel, yellow pear, blackberries, cornucopia border outlined with gilding.

42. A Teacup and Saucer,
painted with flowers and fruit within narrow, gilt bordered cloud-shaped cartouches reserved on a *bleu céleste* ground. On the base of the cup are two mushrooms painted in puce.
c. 1765-68.
Diameter of saucer: 13 cm, height of cup: 4.7 cm.
Marks: crossed swords and *9* with a dot in under-glaze blue.
Provenance: the Anthony Wood Collection.

Giles features: pink rose, convolvulus, yellow and deep purple pear, gooseberries, rosehips, mushrooms, gilded sides to cup handle, chevrons of diminishing size becoming dots down the back.

43. A Plate,
painted with flowers and fruit below an irregular, *bleu céleste* border.
c. 1765-70.
Diameter: 22.2 cm.   Mark: none.

Giles features: pink rose, auriculas, convolvulus, plums, cornucopia border outlined in gilt, ciselé gilding.

40

41

42   43

44. A Dish,

of lozenge shape, painted with fruit, flowers and mushrooms below an irregular claret border.
The Hope-Edwards pattern.
c. 1765-68.
Width: 32.1 cm.   Mark: none.
Lent by: The Bowes Museum, Barnard Castle, the Lady Ludlow Collection; gift of the National Art Collections Fund.

Claret is the one of the rarest of the Giles ground colours and is found only on this dessert service and a small number of tea services, - see the sugar bowl and cover, no. 62.
Giles features: tulip, convolvulus with trailing tendril, purple pear, gooseberries, cornucopia border outlined in gilt, ciselé gilding

45. A Teacup and Saucer,

painted with fruit and flowers in colours below an irregularly shaped purple scale border outlined in gilt.
c. 1765-70.
Diameter of saucer: 12.8 cm, height of cup: 4.6 cm.
Mark: crossed swords and *9* with dot in under-glaze blue.
Lent by: The Ashmolean Museum, Oxford; (Marshall Gift through the National Art Collections Fund, 1957).
Literature: illustrated in Marshall, op. cit., plate 17, no. 309.

Giles features: convolvulus, sliced apple, yellow and purple pears, rosehips, cornucopia border outlined in gilt, gilt dots on back of handle.

46. A Coffee Cup,

decorated with fruit and flowers in colours, with a bunch of rose hips on the reverse and a spray of flowers inside on the base.
1765-70.
Height: 7.6 cm.   Mark: crossed swords and *9* with dot in under-glaze blue.

Giles features: tulip with divergent petals, auriculas, apple, plums, rosehips, dots of diminishing size down back of handle.

II (b) Fruit alone and with Insects

47. A Plate,

painted in colour with different fruits in the centre, and fruits and butterflies on the rim.
c.1763-68.
Diameter: 19.2 cm.   Mark: a red anchor.

Although the inspiration for this style of decoration was ultimately Meissen, the red anchor mark suggests that Giles's painters were more directly influenced by the Chelsea version of this pattern.
Giles features: sliced apple, plums, damsons, blackberries, butterfly, bug.

44. Courtesy of The Bowes Museum, Barnard Castle

45. Courtesy of the Ashmolean Museum, Oxford   46   47

48. A Sweetmeat or Pickle Dish,
moulded in the shape of shell with a deep pink border and two plums and leaves in the centre.
c.1763-68.
Width: 12.5 cm.   Mark: none.

This form was first produced at Lund's Bristol Factory, and then at Worcester in the late 1750's. The only other English factory to make them was John Pennington's Liverpool factory.
Giles features: plums, gilt dots of diminishing size on the handle.

49. A Leaf Dish,
shaped and moulded in the form of a cabbage leaf and painted with a broad green border. In the centre are two brightly coloured butterflies and a spray of fruit.
c. 1763-68.
Length: 21cm.   Mark: none.

This shape is derived from Meissen and was used at Chelsea and Bow and more rarely at Derby. It was manufactured at Worcester from the late 1750's until about 1770. A Factory decorated example with the green border and mauve veins only is illustrated in Albert Amor's exhibition catalogue, *A Celebration-250 Years of Worcester Porcelain*, no. 18, where it is shown as the stand for a cauliflower tureen. It is, possible that Giles simply added the butterflies and fruit to an otherwise Factory decorated piece, but it is clear that Giles also had access to undecorated dishes of this shape from examples that exist and were clearly decorated in his workshop.
Lot 88 of Christie's 1774 sale of Giles's stock is described as 'four colliflower leaves painted'.
Giles features: apple, cherries, butterflies.

50. A Dish,
of oval shape with a bright green rim, moulded with matching pairs of cartouches, and painted in colours with fruits, butterflies and a beetle.
c.1760-65.
Length: 23 cm.   Mark: none.
Provenance: the Dr H J Elverson Collection.

This is a rare form, and there is no identically shaped and moulded example in the major collections. The green border is also a most unusual feature. Another example, also similarly decorated in the Giles workshop, does exist, but with a gilt instead of a bright green border on the rim.
Giles features: apple, damsons, red currants, two butterflies, beetle.

51. A Coffee Pot and Cover,
pear-shaped, painted with bunches of fruits and leaves with a butterfly hovering above.
c. 1762-5.
Height: 14.6 cm.   Mark: none.
Lender: the cover lent by the Museum of Worcester Porcelain.

Literature: a coffee pot and cover of different shape but very similar decoration was lot 235 in Bonhams sale of the Zorensky Collection on 16th March 2004, and is illustrated in the catalogue. The cover is illustrated in Coke, op. cit., plate 63(a) where it is shown on a coffee pot with bird decoration.
Giles features: apple, sliced pear, plums, gilt rims, dots of diminishing size down handle.

48   49

50   51

Of all the different styles of decoration which James Giles employed during the thirty or so years of his workshop's existence, probably the one for which he is now most famous is that featuring exotic birds, or 'fancy birds' as they were called at the time. Gerald Coke[1], for example, considered that, 'The exotic bird designs are perhaps Giles' finest contribution to porcelain decoration'. They must also have been among his most popular designs with his contemporary market, since they first appear on Chinese porcelain of the 1750's and continue right up until Giles's retirement from the decorating business in the mid-1770's.

Giles's fancy birds are fantastic, imaginary creatures, with brilliantly coloured plumage and long tail feathers. Most of them are never seen in flight, but they are often found standing on yellow rocks or ground, or perched on branches. Fancy bird decoration was first used on English porcelain by the Chelsea Factory in the red anchor period of the 1750's, and this was the source of Giles's decoration in the same style.

Good examples of Giles's fancy birds on Chinese porcelain are found on the mug, no. 52, where a typical bird is shown standing on a bare rock with its back half turned towards us so that its magnificent tail and partially extended wing plumage can be displayed to best advantage. This is a pose which is repeated time and again by Giles, and is found on the saucer dish and tea canister from a different service of Chinese porcelain, nos. 53 and 54. Also of Chinese porcelain is the milk jug, no. 55, painted in puce monochrome with a different type of bird, but a very typical Giles butterfly.

Probably one of Giles's earliest fancy birds on Worcester porcelain is that on the mug, no. 56. Thereafter they appear on every variety of ware, in their familiar pose, in the centre of plates and dishes, with borders of flowers or fruits, or in pairs or singly on branches on the rims of plates with fruit in the centre. One of the most beautiful examples is the junket dish, no. 61, with a bird in the centre and another bird, insects and fruit around the rim. The plate, no. 60, is painted with different birds: for once they are in flight, and enclosed within panels outlined in blue and gilt and copied from Sèvres. Different birds again appear in the panels of the celebrated claret ground tea service, no. 62.

Judging by the different variations that were made and the number of examples that have survived, the most popular of the fancy bird patterns was that now known as the 'Lady Mary Wortley Montagu' pattern, in which fancy birds are combined with blue-scale grounds and fine *ciselé* gilding. It first appears in subdued form with modest gilding on a Bow service, a plate from which is in the exhibition, no. 63. Lady Mary died in 1762, at least three or four years before the first Worcester version appeared, so it is possible that her name became associated with the pattern through the Bow version. Gerald Coke identified seven different variants of the pattern on Worcester porcelain, and three of these are in the exhibition, nos. 64-67.

---

[1] *In Search of James Giles,* page 87.

Junket Dish, no. 61.

52. A Mug,
of Chinese porcelain, with under-glaze blue bands around the rim and foot rim, and painted in colours with fancy birds perched on low bushes and standing on rocks surrounded by foliage.
c. 1755-60.
Height: 15 cm.   Marks: none.

Giles features: gilt band round foot rim, yellow rocks or ground with brown edges.

53. A Saucer Dish,
of Chinese porcelain painted in colours with fancy birds surrounded by trees and foliage.
c. 1758-63.
Diameter: 20.6 cm.   Mark: none.
Provenance: the Anthony Wood Collection and the Mottahedah Collection, New York.
Literature: illustrated in David Sanctuary Howard, *China for the West*, no. 549.

The tea canister, no. 54, is probably from the same service.
The large birds are similar to the one on the Worcester mug, no. 56, and the small birds in flight are similar to those on the side of the companion mug, no. 107.
Giles features: gilded birds-eye and sprig border, yellow rocks or ground edged with brown.

54. A Tea Canister and Cover,
of Chinese porcelain painted in colours with two large fancy birds. On the back there are three small birds in flight, and there are four more on the cover.
c. 1758-63.
Height: 14 cm.   Mark: none.
Literature: a teapot stand and some cups and saucers probably from the same service are illustrated in the catalogue of the Graham & Oxley 1981 Summer Exhibition, *English Porcelain Painters of the 18th Century*, nos. 20-24.
The saucer dish, no. 53, is probably from the same service.
Giles features: gilded birds-eye and sprig border, yellow rocks or ground with brown edges.

55. A Milk Jug and Cover,
of Chinese porcelain, decorated in puce with a fancy bird perched on a branch amidst fruit and flowers, with rocks below. There is also a butterfly, and traces of gilt chevrons down the back of the handle.
c. 1755-60.
Height: 12.7 cm.   Mark: none.
Provenance: the Dr H J Elverson Collection.

Giles features: butterfly with folded legs, gilt chevrons on back of handle.

56. A Mug,
painted with a fancy bird within a barbed panel edged with narrow black and iron red lines. On either side of the handle there are sprays of flowers.
c. 1760-65.
Height: 12.1 cm.   Mark: none.
Provenance: the Watney Collection, and Lot 589 in Part II of the Phillips' sale on 10th May 2000.

52

53

54

56

55

This distinctive shape of panel with the black and red border is almost invariably found on mugs, straight-sided or bell-shaped, painted either with a fancy bird and flowers, as here, or with rather crudely painted landscape scenes and birds in green, as no. 107.

The bird in the panel on this mug is similar to those found on nos. 53 and 54.

Giles features: convolvulus with trailing tendril, yellow ground with brown edge.

57. A Dish,

of lozenge shape, painted with a fancy bird surrounded by foliage in the centre. The rim is decorated with fruits, mushrooms and an insect.

c. 1763-68.

Width: 26 cm.   Mark: none.

The plates from this service are marked with a brown anchor, which suggests that this pattern was copied from a Chelsea prototype, which in turn was inspired by a Meissen original.

Giles features: sliced pear, redcurrants, cherries, blackberries, mushrooms, yellow rocks with brown edges.

58. A Plate,

painted in the centre with a fancy bird surrounded by green bushes and a fence. Around the rim there are a spray of flowers and six sprigs of flowers.

c. 1763-68.

Diameter: 22.2 cm.   Mark: none.

Provenance: the Dr H J Elverson Collection.

There are two versions of this pattern, the second having sparser foliage around the bird in the form of a garland, and with more scattered flowers around the rim.

There are also examples of this pattern where there are traces of a crest on the rim at the top of the plate - a pair exhibiting this feature was Lot 305 in the sale of the Rous Lench Collection at Christie's in May 1990.

Giles features: lilies, heartsease, flower x, yellow rocks with brown edges.

59. A Plate,

painted with three pairs of fancy birds, perched on branches amid fruit and foliage. In the centre is a bunch of cherries.

c. 1765-70.

Diameter: 22.2 cm.   Mark: none.

There is also a version of this pattern with single birds only, instead of the pairs as here.

Giles features: cherries; the small flower spray at seven o'clock, added for no obvious reason, is a typically Giles mannerism.

60. A Plate,

painted with fancy birds within three shell-shaped panels, outlined by a scalloped gilt line and edged with bright blue feathering.

c.1770-75.

Diameter: 22.2 cm.   Mark: none.

57   58

59   60

This pattern, copied from Sèvres, is also found on tea services decorated in the Worcester Factory.
Giles features: pink rose, tulip with divergent petals.

61. A Junket Dish,

of fluted shape, decorated with a fancy bird surrounded by green foliage. Around the border there is another bird, perched on a spindly branch, butterflies and fruit.
c. 1765-70.
Diameter: 25 cm.   Mark: none.
Literature: illustrated in the Albert Amor 2000 Exhibition Catalogue *18th Century Porcelain from Renowned Collections,* no. 40.

Giles features: plums, butterflies, yellow rocks edged with brown.

62. A Sugar Bowl and Cover,

painted with large, heart-shaped panels reserved against a rich claret ground decorated with fine *ciselé* gilding and dentil border. Inside the panels are fancy birds on sprays of fruits, and there are three heartsease painted on the inside of the bowl.
c. 1765-68.
Height: 12.5 cm, diameter of cover: 11.2 cm.   Marks: none.

There are two slightly different versions of this service: this one, and one without the dentil edge and with less elaborate gilding on the claret ground. The mottled nature of the claret ground suggests that it was a difficult colour to produce, and may account for the fact that it is one of Giles rarest ground colours.
Giles features: redcurrants, gilt band round the foot rim, ciselé gilding.

63. A Plate,

of Bow porcelain, with mirror-shaped panels painted with pairs of fancy birds, and smaller panels painted with butterflies, reserved against an under-glaze wet blue ground.
c. 1765.
Diameter: 20.9 cm.   Mark: an anchor and dagger in red.
Lent by the Museum of London.

Possibly a precursor which gave its name to the Worcester Lady Mary Wortley Montagu pattern. See the preamble to this section, paragraph 5.
The birds and foliage are similar to those on the Chinese tea wares, nos. 53 and 54.
Giles features: yellow ground with brown edge.

64. A Plate,

painted with three broad, mirror-shaped panels, each painted with a fancy bird, and a central circular panel painted with a spray of flowers, all reserved against an under-glaze blue-scale ground.
The Lady Mary Wortley Montagu pattern.
c. 1770-75.
Diameter: 22.2cm.   Mark: a fretted square in under-glaze blue.
Lent by the Holburne Museum of Art, Bath.

Gerald Coke identified seven different versions of this pattern: this is version no. 2.

61   62

63   Courtesy of the Museum of London   64   Courtesy of the Holburne Museum of Art

This configuration of reserved panels is not found with Worcester Factory decoration, and it is likely that it was specially ordered by Giles.
Giles features: tulip with divergent petals, ciselé gilding, yellow rocks or ground with brown edges.

65. A Dish,
circular, decorated with two large, mirror-shaped panels painted with fancy birds, and smaller panels painted with flowers, reserved against an under-glaze blue-scale ground.
The Lady Mary Wortley Montagu pattern no. 4.
c. 1768-73.
Diameter: 22.2 cm.   Mark: a fretted square in under-glaze blue.

Gerald Coke identified seven different versions of this pattern: this is no. 4 in his classification, and described as 'a rare version'. It is only found on deep dishes of this shape.
The same flower types and grouping in the left hand panel are found in the right hand panel of the Lord Craven pattern plate, no. 19.
Giles features: pink roses, tulip with divergent petals, auriculas, forget-me-nots, convolvulus with trailing tendril, yellow rocks or ground edged with brown, ciselé gilding.

66. A Teacup, Coffee Cup and Saucer,
painted with fancy birds within mirror-shaped panels, and with insects and flowers within smaller panels, reserved against an under-glaze blue-scale ground.
The Lady Mary Wortley Montagu pattern no. 1.
c. 1774-76.
Diameter of saucer: 12.7 cm, height of coffee cup: 7 cm.
Marks: a fretted square on the saucer, and a crescent on the cups, all in under-glaze blue.

Giles features: convolvulus, lilies, yellow rocks edged with brown, ciselé gilding, dots of diminishing size down backs of handles, gilt bands round foot rims, flower spray in bottom of coffee cup.

67. A Chocolate or Coffee Cup,
decorated with two large reserved panels painted with fancy birds and smaller panels painted with flowers or insects, reserved against an under-glaze blue scale ground.
c. 1768-73.
Height: 7.6 cm.   Mark: a fretted square in under-glaze blue.
The Lady Mary Wortley Montagu pattern no.1.

This cup is larger than the standard coffee cup although it can be used with the same saucer. The complete Giles tea and coffee service at Corsham Court contains coffee type cups of both sizes. The late Lord Methuen used to refer to it as 'the breakfast service', and it is possible that the larger cups were simply coffee cups used at breakfast. Alternatively, they may have been used for chocolate.
Giles features: yellow rocks edged with brown, ciselé gilding.

65   67

66

In addition to the fancy birds, Giles also decorated a number of services with 'naturalistic' birds, although the distinction between the two groups is somewhat blurred. One or two tea services are painted with ornithologically accurate birds - bull finches and waders, for example. Another is painted entirely with canaries, see catalogue no. 68, but most of the birds on the other services are not recognisable, and are as much the product of the imagination as the genuinely fancy birds. All these birds, however, are perched on leafy, stringy, brown branches which often appear too flimsy to bear their weight.

This type of decoration is derived, like so much of Giles, from Meissen, and is most commonly found on tea wares. Only one dessert service is recorded, from which a plate in the Marshall Collection, no. 73, is in the exhibition. Naturalistic birds are also found on a garniture of five vases, also in the Marshall Collection, and they appear in the panels of some very rare hexagonal vases.

The acceptance of naturalistic birds into the Giles canon has been a lengthy process. In Chapter 3 of his *Coloured Worcester Porcelain of the First Period* published in 1954, H R Marshall drew up a list of the various different types of decoration which he attributed to the Giles workshop, but he did not include naturalistic bird painting, and the various examples of such birds illustrated in the catalogue in Part 2 of his book are all assumed to be Factory decorated. Similarly, in the second edition of his *Worcester Porcelain and Lund's Bristol* published in 1965, Franklin Barrett simply repeats Marshall's list.

Naturalistic birds were first attributed to the Giles workshop in Albert Amor's 1977 Exhibition, *James Giles China & Enamel Painter*. The reason was that the purple flower sprays in the smaller panels of the blue ground

service, no. 69, are very similar to those found on other Giles services - the 'Golden Fleece' service, no. 82, for example. This attribution was maintained in Albert Amor's second Giles exhibition in 1983, which coincided with the publication of Gerald Coke's book, *In Search of James Giles*. Not everyone agreed, however, and in his review[1] of the book John Mallet wrote: 'one large group of Worcester porcelain that must come under close scrutiny before a Giles attribution is accepted comprises birds on stringy brown branches'.

This question was finally resolved in 1987, when Mrs Anne George published an article entitled *A Question of Attribution,* in the May edition of *The Antique Dealer and Collector's Guide*. Subsequent to the publication of his book, Gerald Coke had acquired a pair of iron-red ground hexagonal vases, and in her article Mrs George was able to demonstrate that the gilding, and the naturalistic bird and flower painting in the panels, matched those on other, indisputably Giles-decorated, objects. Since then there has been a general acceptance that 'the birds on stringy brown branches' were, indeed, painted in the Giles workshop.

A feature of this group of naturalistic bird patterns is the gilding on the three services which have coloured grounds: one under-glaze blue scale, no. 69 and two on-glaze, nos. 72 and 74. This gilding is unlike that found on any other Giles services, and is simple, even naïve, when compared with the rich and elaborate *ciselé* gilding which usually accompanies other Giles services featuring coloured grounds. This would suggest that as a group they can be attributed to the first half to middle of the 1760's, before the workshop acquired the gilding skills for which it later became so famous.

---

[1] *The Burlington Magazine,* November 1984, pages 705-706.

Plate, no. 73. Courtesy of The Ashmolean Museum, Oxford.

68. A Tea Bowl, Coffee Cup and Saucer,
with gilt rims, painted with a canary on a leafy branch and a small flower spray.
c.1762-67.
Diameter of saucer: 12.7 cm, height of coffee cup: 6.5 cm, height of tea bowl: 4.5 cm.   Marks: none.
Provenance: the Anthony Wood Collection.
Literature: illustrated in Robyn Robb, *2003 Exhibition* Catalogue, no. 11.

On all the extant examples of this service the birds on the tea bowl and saucer have black shading, while the bird on the coffee cup is in plain yellow, suggesting that they were painted by different hands.
The flower spray on the bottom of the saucer and the backs of the cups is identical to one found in purple on the 'Golden Fleece' teapot, no. 82.
Giles feature: flower spray in bottom of coffee cup.

69. A Teacup, Coffee Cup and Saucer,
painted with naturalistic birds on spindly, leafy branches and with flower sprigs in puce, within panels reserved against an under-glaze, blue-scale ground.
c.1765-68.
Diameter of saucer: 13 cm, height of coffee cup: 6.5 cm, height of teacup: 5 cm.
Marks: a fretted square in under-glaze blue.
Provenance: teacup and saucer, the Anthony Wood Collection.

70. A Mug,
of small size, painted with a naturalistic bird in blue, orange and yellow, standing on a leafy branch. There is a butterfly on the back.
c. 1762-67.
Height: 6.25 cm.   Mark: none.
Exhibited: Albert Amor's 2001 Exhibition, *A Celebration - 250 Years of Worcester Porcelain*, no. 40.

It is not clear whether these little mugs or cans were included in tea and coffee services in place of the more usual coffee cups. For another example, compare no. 8, in this exhibition.

71. A Teacup and Saucer,
decorated with brightly coloured naturalistic birds perched on stringy branches, below a deep yellow irregular border. There is a single mauve flower spray on the bottom of the saucer and the back of the cup.
c.1762-67.
Diameter of saucer: 13.5 cm, height of cup: 4.5 cm.
Marks: crossed swords and *9* with a dot in under-glaze blue.
Provenance: the Dr H J Elverson and Perrins Collections.

The mauve, honeysuckle-like flower spray is also found on the 'Golden Fleece' teapot, no. 82.

68   69

70   71

72. A Teacup and Saucer,
with an uneven sea green ground and reserved panels painted with naturalistic birds on branches. The handle has gilt dots down its back, and the base of the cup is painted inside with green leaves.
c.1762-67.
Diameter of saucer: 13 cm, height of cup: 4.8 cm.
Mark: crossed swords and *9* with dot in under-glaze blue.

Giles features: gilt band round foot rim, gilt dots down back of handle.

73. A Plate,
decorated with a blue-green leaf spray border, and in the centre a naturalistic bird, painted in colours, perched upon a leafy bough.
c. 1762-67.
Diameter: 19.1 cm.   Mark: none.
Lent by: The Ashmolean Museum, Oxford; (Marshall Gift through the National Art Collections Fund, 1957).
Literature: illustrated in Marshall, op. cit., plate 31, no. 689.

Naturalistic bird decoration is mainly found on tea wares, and this appears to be the only dessert service painted in this style. A pair of plates from this service was in the Rous Lench Collection, and was Lot 303 in the Christie's sale in May 1990.

74. A Teacup,
painted with naturalistic birds sitting on thin branches in panels reserved against a sea-green ground, outlined with a scalloped gilt line.
c.1762-67.
Height: 5 cm.   Mark: crossed sword and *9* with dot in under-glaze blue.

Giles features: gilt band round foot rim.

72   73

73. Courtesy of The Ashmolean Museum, Oxford.

Between 1700 and 1830 some six thousand Chinese armorial services were imported into Europe, most of which came to the British Isles. The market for armorial wares was, therefore, huge and one in which, on the face of it, James Giles had a number of important competitive advantages. Firstly, there was a delay of at least two years between the ordering of an armorial service from China and its delivery, whereas Giles could presumably produce a service in a matter of months, if not weeks. He had access to undecorated Chinese porcelain in the early years of his enterprise, and subsequently to Worcester porcelain, which by then had been developed to a high quality, and, unique among English factories at that period, was able to withstand heat. He was based in London which was the centre of the fashionable world, and would facilitate ordering and delivery. He had established a good reputation for the quality of his work. The market for armorial porcelain cannot have been particularly price-sensitive, and in any case, the rest of his product range clearly sold, so that although Chinese-decorated wares were cheaper than Giles's, it seems unlikely that this would have been an overriding consideration.

Given these advantages, the total of less than twenty examples of Giles armorial decoration so far recorded seems surprisingly small. The list of clients in his ledger contains many families who were armigerous, and yet, assuming it is a complete record of his credit sales, he carried out no armorial decoration during the years 1771-76, with the possible exception of a one-off sample plate for the Duke of Portland.

As with other types of decoration, the earliest armorial services attributed to his workshop are on Chinese porcelain. No. 75 is a pair of plates painted with the crest of the Sealy family, which are of particular interest because they bear traces of the gilt border found on Grubbe plate 1. No. 76, the sugar bowl from the Hayes service, and no. 77, a coffee cup painted with the arms of Acclom, were certainly decorated by the same hand, and probably in the Giles workshop, although they do not bear any of the Giles mannerisms which would make such an attribution certain. On the other hand three examples on Worcester porcelain - plates from the Gavin/Hearsey and the Calmady services, and a trio from the Beaumont/Ayscough tea service - may confidently be attributed to the workshop.

In addition to painting complete armorial services, Giles is known to have decorated a number of one-off teapots and bowls, and two pairs of mugs. The teapots were probably made to be used with different cups and saucers etc., while the bowls may have been decorated as samples, to enable a prospective customer to decide if a complete service was required. The same may have been true of the plate referred to above bearing the arms of the Duke of Portland, which is now in the Ashmolean Museum. It is the only known example, which makes it doubtful if there was ever a complete service. The pairs of mugs appear to have been made to commemorate special events. One of them, no. 80, is decorated with the arms of Martindale, and dated under the foot rim. The dating suggests some special occasion for the Martindale family: unfortunately we have no idea what that might have been.

Finally, included in this section is the teapot, no. 82, from the well known service whose main decoration is a golden ram suspended by a chain.

Plate, no. 78.

75. A Pair of Plates,
of Chinese porcelain, each painted in colours with flowers, a vegetable and insects. On the top is a crest and around the rim there are clear traces of an elaborate gilt border, identical to that on Grubbe plate 1.
c.1755-60.
Width: 23 cm.   Mark: none.
The crest is that of Sealy, *a talbot sejant proper collared and chained or.*
Provenance: the Watney Collection and lot 811in Part III of the Phillips' sale on 1st November 2000.
Literature: the left hand plate is illustrated in David Sanctuary Howard, *Chinese Armorial Porcelain*, Vol. II, page 19, and the companion plate on page 283.

The catalogue entry in the Watney sale states that 'the floral sprigs on these plates show affinity with later painting attributed to the James Giles workshop, making a Giles attribution probable'. The subsequent discovery of the traces of the Grubbe border must make such an attribution more probable, although it is not clear precisely what significance to attach to its presence.
Giles features: pink roses, tulip with divergent petals, traces of Grubbe plate 1 type border on rim.

76. A Sugar Bowl,
of Chinese porcelain, decorated in London and probably in the Giles workshop, with a coat of arms on the front and a crest on the back.
c.1757-62.
Diameter: 11.7 cm.   Mark: none.
The arms are those of Hayes, *erminois three wolves' heads erased sable*, with crest, *a wolf passant erminois.*
Provenance: the Frederick Arthur Crisp and Phil Cooke Collections. A teacup, a coffee cup and a saucer from the same service are in the Victoria & Albert Museum, and the teapot is in the Metropolitan Museum, New York.

In *The Language of Flowers*, ECC Transactions, Vol. 16, part 1, 1996, page 4, Dr Bernard Watney refers to 'an earlier Chinese service bearing the arms of the Hayes family of London which is here considered to be early Giles'. This attribution was based on the flowers surrounding the arms which are by the same hand as those on the coffee cup, no. 77.

77. A Coffee Cup,
of Chinese porcelain, decorated in London and probably in the Giles workshop, with a coat of arms and crest, and a flower spray inside on the bottom.
c. 1757-62.
Height: 7.5 cm.   Mark: none.
The arms are those of Acclom, *gules a maunch argent within an orle of cinquefoils of the last*, quartering Pokesworth, *or three dragons' heads couped gules.* The impaled coat is unknown, *azure a chevron argent in base a mullet of six points of the last.* The crest is not recorded for either Acclom or Pokesworth, *a cubit arm habited.*
Literature: illustrated in David Sanctuary Howard, *Chinese Armorial Porcelain*, Vol. II, page 708.
Exhibited: *East Meets West: Oriental Porcelain Decorated in Europe*, British Museum, September 2001-March 2002.

No other item from this service is recorded.

75

76   77

The probable Giles attribution is based on the flowers around the coat, which are by the same hand as similar flowers around the coat on the Hayes service, no. 76. The absence of gilding is unusual, but Giles's gilding tends to rub easily on Chinese hard paste porcelain, and it may simply have disappeared. *Giles feature: a flower spray in the bottom.*

78. A Plate,

painted with a coat of arms and a crest, set in an elaborate mantling of iron red and silver. Around the rim are purple flower sprays.
c. 1762-1767.
Diameter: 22 cm.   Mark: none.
The arms are those of Gavin, *argent a sword in pale azure ensigned with a mullet gules surmounted by a saltire couped sable,* with crest, *a two-masted sailing ship flying the blue ensign.* The impaled arms are those of Hearsey, *gules a chief argent.*

David Gavin, a wealthy tailor living in Holland, married Christina Hearsey in 1751. She died in 1767, and Gavin married secondly the Lady Elizabeth Maitland, daughter of the 7th Earl of Lauderdale, in 1770. On armorial grounds, therefore, this service must pre-date Gavin's second marriage in 1770, and most probably Christina's death in 1767.
Giles features: winter jasmine, lilies of the valley.

79. A Teacup, a Coffee Cup and a Saucer,

the saucer painted with a coat of arms and crest and the cups with the crest only. Each is also painted with sprays of winter jasmine in natural colours.
c.1762-67.
Diameter of saucer: 12.75 cm, height of teacup: 4.5 cm, height of coffee cup: 6.3 cm.
Marks: teacup and saucer: crossed swords, figure *9* and dot in under-glaze blue, coffee cup: none.
The arms are those of Beaumont, *gules a lion rampant argent, armed and langued azure, between eight crescents in orle or,* with crest, *a bull's head erased quarterly argent and gules.* The arms in pretence are those of Ayscough, *sable a fess between three asses passant argent.*
Provenance: the Anthony Wood Collection.

The purple honeycomb border around the coat of arms is very similar to that around the coat of the Gavin/Hearsey service, no. 78.
Giles features: winter jasmine sprays, flower spray in bottom of coffee cup.

80. A Mug,

painted with a coat of arms, the shield supported by a naked boy, shrouded by a blue scarf, and surrounded by sprays of flowers in gilt. On the base are inscribed the initials *JM* and the date *April 5, 1770,* also in gilt.
c.1770.
Height: 15.3 cm.   Mark: none.
The arms are those of Martindale, *barry of six argent and gules, overall a bend sable.*
Motto: *MERITE FORTUNE.*
Lent by: The Ashmolean Museum, Oxford; (Marshall Gift through the National Art Collections Fund, 1957).
Literature: illustrated in Marshall, op. cit., plate 36, no. 783.

78   79

80   Courtesy of the Ashmolean Museum, Oxford

This mug is one of a pair; the companion is in the Victoria & Albert Museum.

The use of the arms, the date and the style of decoration all suggest that the mugs were decorated by Giles to commemorate some special event in John Martindale's life. Unfortunately we do not know the significance of the date, 5th April 1770. Giles's ledger shows that Martindale bought fifteen parcels of china and two of glass during the years 1771-74, though clearly none of these purchases was this pair of mugs.

Giles features: gilt band round foot rim, gilding on the sides of the handle and chevrons down the back.

81. A Plate,

in the well is a coat of arms surmounted by a crest and flanked by flowers, with the initials *WC* inscribed on a blue ribbon below.

c. 1765-70.

Diameter: 22 cm.   Mark: none.

The arms are those of Calmady, *azure, a chevron between three pears or,* with crest, *a winged horse argent.*

Literature: a teacup and saucer with the same arms and decoration are illustrated in Spero and Sandon, op. cit., no. 454.

This service was probably made for Captain Warwick Calmady (1711-88) or his son, also Warwick, who died in 1780. This service was unrecorded until the remaining pieces were sold by the descendants of the Calmady family at Bearne's salerooms in May 1985.

Giles features: characteristic dots of diminishing size down the backs, and gilding on the sides, of the handles of tea and coffee cups of the same pattern.

82. A Teapot and Cover,

of globular shape, painted with a gilded ram suspended from a chain attached to a belt around its body, surrounded by scattered flowers in pink monochrome.

c. 1765-68.

Height: 13.5 cm.   Mark: none.

Provenance: the Zorensky Collection, and sold at Bonhams in Part I of the sale of the Collection on 16th March 2004, lot 244.

Literature: illustrated in Spero and Sandon, op. cit., no. 443.

The late David Howard has kindly researched this emblem, and supplied the following information, 'The device with a sheep or fleece is not heraldic and is not recorded in any work on heraldry in the form shown. The wool trade was among the most prosperous in London from the Middle Ages, however, and a member of the Woolmens', Woolmongers', Woolpackers', Woolwinders' or Wool Staplers' Companies may have had this made specially (although it is NOT the crest of any of these). In the 18th century a number of wealthy inns and hotels, many of which had custom-made porcelain with their device, were called 'The Golden Fleece', including one in Covent Garden, and it may have been one of these. A very similar device with a fleece hanging from a ring is part of the shield of the City of Leeds. It is also possible that a rich wool merchant or woollen draper may have commissioned Giles'.

81

82

During the last thirty years or so of the eighteenth century the fashionable world in England was gripped by what Josiah Wedgwood called 'Vase madness', and the market responded with a huge increase in vase production, not only by pottery and porcelain makers, but also by architects, painters and manufacturers in metals. This demand was inspired, ultimately, by the excavations at Pompeii and Herculaneum and the consequent revival in classical taste. However, as Sir Timothy Clifford has pointed out[1], 'Apparently 'the man of taste' of the 1760s and 1770s did not care to have his house furnished according to the tenets of strict archaeological accuracy.... He wanted rather the spirit of classical art reproduced in his house than the letter.... So patrons and manufacturers turned to designs more acceptable to themselves made by renaissance, mannerist, or even late seventeenth and early eighteenth century artists'.

Although Wedgwood's description of this phenomenon was 'Vase madness', in a letter to his partner Thomas Bentley in 1768 he comments, ' "Urns a better name" - very true, call them so', and goes on to distinguish between the two - 'the character of Urns is simplicity, to have covers, but no handles, nor spouts, they are monumental, they may be either high or low, but should not seem to be Vessels for culinary, or sacred uses. - Vases are such as might be used for libations, & other sacrificial, festive & culinary uses, such as Ewers, open vessels &c.'

Giles responded to this latest whim of fashionable taste by producing a number of dessert and tea services painted with different urns enclosed within borders, made up either of coloured bands decorated with grapes and vine leaves in gilt, or of bands of trailing foliage. For his urn designs he turned to an eighteenth century sculptor, Jacques Saly, born in Valenciennes in 1717 and apprenticed in 1738. In 1740 Saly won a scholarship to Rome, where in 1746 he etched a series of thirty plates of urns. Sets of these plates were owned by the architects Sir William Chambers and Robert Adam, and Giles evidently had access to a set, since a number of the vases painted on his services are clearly based on Saly's designs. Examples from four of Giles's dessert services and one of his tea sets are in the exhibition. They belong to the period from 1770 to 1775.

Lot 53 on the first day of Christie's 1774 sale is described as 'A pair of caudle cups, covers and stands enamel'd in compartments with antique vases green and crimson with gold curtains'. Unfortunately, for it must have been a striking pattern, no example fitting this description is known. However, Lot 57 on the last day, 'a desert service elegantly painted with different vases and an ultramarine border....' clearly refers to no. 83 or no. 84.

---

[1] Sir Timothy Clifford, ECC Transactions, Vol. 10, Part 3, *Some English Ceramic Vases and their Sources, Part 1,* page 159.

Dish, no. 85.

83. A Pair of Plates,
painted in the centre with an urn swathed with wreaths of flowers. The rim is painted with an over-glaze blue band decorated with grapes and vine leaves in gilt, and on the inside there is a formal gilt border.
c. 1770-75.
Diameter: 22.3 cm.   Mark: none.

Lot 57 of the fifth day of Christie's 1774 sale is described as 'a desert service elegantly painted with different vases and an ultramarine blue border, enriched with chased and burnished gold'. This must refer to this pattern or to no. 84. The blue of the border is a most unusual colour.
Giles features: ciselé gilding.

84 . A Dish,
of square shape, painted with an urn with coloured flower sprays around the top. The rim is painted with an under-glaze blue band, on which is a continuous gilt pattern of grapes and vine leaves.
c. 1774-76.
Width: 21.6 cm.   Mark: a crescent in under-glaze blue.

See comment on no. 83 re Lot 57 of the fifth day of Christie's 1774 sale. This must refer to this pattern or to no. 83.
This is the smaller of the two square dessert dishes made at Worcester.
Giles features: ciselé gilding.

85. A Dish,
of deep, square shape, painted in the well with an urn with a satyr mask and snake handles, draped with floral swags. Around the rim there is a wavy border of naturalistic foliage.
c. 1770-75.
Width: 24.1 cm.   Mark: none.

This is the larger of the two square dessert dishes made at Worcester.

86. A Plate,
painted in the well with an urn with two mask handles wreathed with garlands of flowers. Around the rim is a border made up of a chocolate-brown band entwined with a continuous garland of leaves.
c. 1770-75.
Diameter: 22.1 cm.   Mark: none.

The same border is found on dessert and tea services decorated with flowers, nos. 11 and 12.

87. A Teacup and Saucer,
painted with different urns within the larger mirror-shaped panels, and with flowers within the smaller panels, all reserved against an under-scale blue scale ground decorated with delicate gilding.
c.1774-76.
Diameter of saucer: 12.75 cm, height of cup: 4.5 cm.   Mark: a crescent in under-glaze blue.
Literature: a teacup and saucer of the same pattern are illustrated in Spero and Sandon, op. cit. no. 429, but are marked with a fretted square in under-glaze blue.

Giles features: lily, dots of diminishing size down backs of handles.

83   84   83

85   87   86

Many of Giles's landscape scenes include human figures, but the workshop also painted a small number of services on which they are the principal form of decoration. The commonest are rustic figures, usually described as 'in the manner of David Teniers'. Teniers established a style of painting which had many imitators, and which continued over many years through reproduction in prints, tapestries and other decorative objects. It is likely that prints were Giles's source for these figures.

Their attribution to the Giles workshop is based on the two Grubbe tea canisters, which were described in Chapter 2, and each of which has such a figure painted in one of its main panels. One now in the Marshall Collection is no. 92 in this exhibition, and has a girl blowing bubbles, while the second, from the Museum of Worcester Porcelain, shows a boy catching a butterfly. Early examples of these figures are found on a mixed service of Chinese and Worcester porcelain. The Worcester sugar bowl shows a girl washing clothes in a stream, and the cover has a boy seated at a table, while the Chinese tea canister has a delightful picture of a girl dancing. The Worcester coffee cup and Chinese saucer, no. 88, may have come from this service. In the Royal Collection there is a part tea service of this pattern, including a teapot, a milk jug, a slop basin, and four teacups and saucers, all of Worcester porcelain and embellished with fine Giles gilding, and at least two other Worcester teapots painted with similar figures are known. This suggests that there were a number of all Worcester services as well as the one of mixed porcelain referred to above.

The Teniers-type figures are country folk engaged in homely activities: higher up the social scale are the figures on the pair of vases, no. 89, which were probably originally from a garniture of three - the Museum of Fine Arts in Boston has such a set. The figures are of children masquerading as adults, and, with their ruffs, cloaks and pointed collars, they are wearing clothes which had been long out of fashion. They are reading, playing musical instruments and fanning themselves, rather than washing clothes or smoking pipes. They are most probably French in origin, and in a style typical of several French painters of the eighteenth century, including Lancret, Pater, and Watteau. Again, Giles probably copied them from prints, or possibly a pattern book.

The figure of the boy playing a box guitar on the left hand vase is also found in the group of three figures in the centre of the large oblong dish or tray with the saxe-blue border, no. 91. The scene is painted in iron red monochrome, and is reminiscent of the *fete champêtre* paintings of Watteau. The only other examples of this type of decoration are a pair of teacups and saucers, and it is likely that they were all once part of the same cabaret set.

Finally, the sugar bowl and cover, no. 90, is from one of the finest and rarest of all Giles services. The coloured ground is the only recorded use by Giles of under-glaze powder blue, and in the reserved panels are figures of musicians playing different instruments. They are wearing made-up, 'pastoral' clothes, and the bagpipes which the man on the bowl is playing are also a 'shepherd' accoutrement. Again, these figures are French in origin, but earlier, less mannered, and closer to the original paintings than the figures on the vases.

Dish, no. 91. Courtesy of the Ashmolean Museum, Oxford

88. A Coffee Cup and Saucer,
the saucer of Chinese porcelain, the cup of Worcester porcelain, painted with figures in the manner of David Teniers.
c. 1760-65.
Diameter of saucer: 11.9 cm, height of cup: 6.5 cm.   Marks: none.
Lent by: The Ashmolean Museum, Oxford; (Marshall Gift through the National Art Collections Fund, 1957).
Literature: illustrated in Marshall, op. cit., plate 19, no. 348.

This pattern is one of the three known examples of Giles decorated tea services made up of both Chinese and Worcester porcelain. The evidence in this case is a service of 23 pieces which was sold at Puttick and Simpson's in 1963. It was made up of 9 pieces of Worcester including a milk jug, a sugar bowl, a slop basin, and six coffee cups, and 14 pieces of Chinese porcelain, including a tea canister, 9 tea bowls, and 4 saucers. This cup and saucer may have been from this service.

89. A Pair of Vases,
possibly of Bow porcelain, of baluster shape, painted with richly dressed European figures in wooded landscapes within panels, reserved against a dry blue ground, decorated with flower sprays in *ciselé* gilding.
c. 1763-68.
Height: 12.7 cm.   Marks: a 'G' in under-glaze blue on one vase only.
Provenance: the Anthony Wood Collection.
Literature: illustrated in Robyn Robb, *2003 Exhibition* Catalogue, no. 6.
Exhibited: the 1999 International Ceramics Fair Loan Exhibition, no. 87.

There is some question as to which English porcelain factory produced these vases. They were sold at Christie's on 27th April 1998, Lot 26, where they were catalogued as Vauxhall, but at the International Ceramics Fair in the following year they were attributed to the Bow factory. Coke illustrates a vase of different shape, but with very similar decoration, in *In Search of James Giles*, plate 44 (b), which he attributes to Bow. Moreover, in the Museum of Fine Arts in Boston there is a garniture of three vases made up of a pair of similar shape to these and one similar to that illustrated by Coke. All three are decorated with different, but similar European figures to these and again are attributed to Bow. A Bow attribution for these vases does, therefore, seem most likely.
One of the figures is very similar to that of the musician on the large dish, no. 91, and each was clearly copied from the same source.
This shape of vase was first produced at Vincennes in the 1750's.
Giles features: ciselé gilding.

90. A Sugar Bowl and Cover,
decorated with three fan shaped panels and three small circular panels, reserved against a powder blue ground, and painted in colours with European figures playing musical instruments and insects. There is a spray of cherries on the base of the bowl.
The Lord Dudley service.
c. 1765-68.
Height: 10.5 cm.   Mark: none.
Lent by: The Ashmolean Museum, Oxford; (Marshall Gift through the National Art Collections Fund, 1957).

89

88 Courtesy of the Ashmolean Museum, Oxford.   90 Courtesy of the Ashmolean Museum, Oxford.

Literature: illustrated in Dinah Reynolds, *Worcester Porcelain in the Ashmolean Museum*, plate 31, no. 126.

Powder blue was introduced by the Worcester factory in the mid-1760's, and was probably the first under-glaze blue ground colour to be used. It was evidently not a colour favoured by Giles as this is the only service recorded which uses it.

This sucrier was one of the items in a part service belonging to the Earl of Dudley, which was sold in 1924.

A spoon tray with similar decoration but a blue-scale ground is illustrated in Coke, op. cit., plate 41 (b).

Giles features: gilt band round the foot rim, ciselé gilding, butterflies.

91. A Dish or Tray,

of oblong, octagonal shape, with a broad, saxe-blue scale border, from which are suspended four sprays of flowers. In the centre, in a wooded landscape there are a seated lady and gentleman, with a musician playing beside them, all painted in iron red monochrome.

c. 1765-68.

Length: 33.8 cm. Mark: none.

Lent by: The Ashmolean Museum, Oxford; (Marshall Gift through the National Art Collections Fund, 1957).

Literature: illustrated in Marshall, op. cit., plate 20, no. 367.

Exhibited: Albert Amor 1977 Exhibition, *James Giles, China Painter*, no. 42.

There are only two teacups and saucers recorded in this rare form of decoration, one of which is now in the Museum of Worcester Porcelain. Given that the only other pieces similarly decorated are tea wares, it is possible that this dish was in fact the tray of a cabaret of which the cups and saucers were also part.

Giles features: convolvulus with trailing tendril, auriculas, cornucopia-shaped border outlined in gilt.

92. A Tea Canister,

decorated with two large panels and four small panels, reserved against an under-glaze scale-blue ground. In one panel there is a girl sitting on a rock, blowing bubbles: in the other a bouquet of flowers and fruit including a sliced pear. There are flower sprays in the small panels.

c. 1765-70.

Height: 12 cm. Mark: a fretted square in under-glaze blue.

Lent by: The Ashmolean Museum, Oxford; (Marshall Gift through the National Art Collections Fund, 1957).

Literature: illustrated in Dinah Reynolds, *Worcester Porcelain in the Ashmolean Museum*, plate 29, no. 127 and in Marshall, op. cit., colour plate 10.

One of the two matching tea canisters sold by Miss M J M Grubbe, a direct descendant of James Giles, at Sotheby's on 13th May 1952. The canisters, together with the four Grubbe plates, are recognised as having been painted in the Giles workshop, and are the foundation on which almost all subsequent attributions to the workshop are made.

The style of figure painting in the manner of David Teniers is very similar to that on the cup and saucer, no. 88.

Giles features: pink rose, sliced pair, gilt band round foot rim, ciselé gilding.

91 Courtesy of the Ashmolean Museum

92 Courtesy of the Ashmolean Museum, Oxford.

Giles's 1763 advertisement in *The Universal Director* states that he copied the pattern of any china 'either in the European or Chinese Taste'. From the decoration of the Grubbe plates and tea canisters it has been possible to build up a fairly complete picture of his work 'in the European Taste', but unfortunately they give us no help in identifying his work in the oriental style.

The evidence of contemporary sale catalogues, however, suggests that his output of services decorated in oriental patterns was quite small. Thus, out of a total of five hundred and seventy-three lots in Christie's sale in December 1769, only thirty-two, or less than six percent, have descriptions which clearly refer to oriental patterns. Similarly, in the March 1774 sale, there are only fifteen lots out of a total of four hundred and fifty, or just over three percent, which are described with oriental patterns - 'old japan pattern' or 'old wheat sheaf pattern', for example. This suggests that, at any rate during the last years of his workshop's existence, services in oriental patterns were a small and possibly declining proportion of his total decorating output.

Nevertheless, Giles undoubtedly painted some porcelain 'in the Chinese Taste' and in default of other evidence various methods of attributing oriental patterns to his workshop have evolved. Firstly, there are a number of *Imari* patterns found on Worcester porcelain, some direct copies of Japanese originals. Where the blue on these pieces has been applied under the glaze - as was the case on the oriental prototypes - it is assumed that they were painted at the Worcester Factory, since no outside decorator was able to do this for technical reasons. On those pieces where the blue has been applied on-glaze like the other enamel colours, this is taken as evidence of outside decoration. Since Giles was the only outside decorator known to have bought large quantities of undecorated porcelain from Worcester, the probability is that such pieces were decorated by him. The teapot, no. 93, and the plate, no. 94, are tentatively attributed to his workshop on these grounds.

Secondly, there are a small number of oriental patterns of which two different versions are found on Worcester porcelain. An example is the so-called *Phoenix* pattern, no. 96. The basis for attribution here is that two different versions presuppose two different sources, since the Worcester Factory, say, would hardly go to the trouble of producing two similar versions of the same pattern. In that situation the most likely second source is the Giles workshop.

Finally, there are a number of patterns whose inspiration is clearly oriental, but which are considered more likely to have been decorated in the Giles workshop than the Worcester Factory on stylistic grounds. Examples are the bowl, no. 95, and the teapot, no. 97.

None of the pieces in this section of the exhibition can be attributed to the Giles workshop with certainty, and unless some new evidence comes to light, the attribution of oriental patterns to the workshop will continue to be fraught with uncertainty.

Junket Dish, no. 96.

93. A Teapot,

of globular, fluted form, painted in Imari style with sprays of Oriental flowers and grasses in red, gold and on-glaze blue.

c. 1765-70.

Height: 15.2 cm.   Mark: a fretted square in under-glaze blue.

There does not appear to be another example of this pattern recorded.

The use of on-glaze blue decoration, especially in conjunction with the Worcester Factory's under-glaze blue fretted square mark, strongly suggests outside decoration. This need not necessarily have been carried out at the Giles workshop, but the quality and sophistication of the decoration, and the fact that Giles was buying quantities of undecorated Worcester at that time, make such an attribution more than possible.

94. A Plate,

painted in Imari style with a central vase of flowers and borders of trailing foliage, prunus and pine in on-glaze blue, red, pink and gold.

c. 1765-70.

Diameter: 22.2 cm.
                                                            Mark: none.

The decoration on this plate is copied directly from a Japanese Imari original of the early eighteenth century, an example of which is in the British Museum. The blue on the latter is painted under-glaze, while that on this Worcester version is over-glaze, strongly suggesting that this is outside rather than Factory decoration. This need not necessarily have been carried out at the Giles workshop, but, as in the case of the teapot, no. 94, such an attribution is probable.

This pattern is not found on objects other than plates of this size. There are a number of examples in existence, which suggests that there may have been a service of this pattern, or possibly that they were made to supplement a Japanese service.

95. A Bowl,

Decorated in Japanese style with four panels, two painted with Oriental figures and two with formalised flowers in over-glaze blue. Between them are four narrower panels of orange colour, diapered with gilding, each having a white chrysanthemum mons. At the top of the foot rim is an over-glaze blue and gilt border.

c.1765-70.

Diameter: 15 cm, height: 6.5 cm.   Mark: none.

Lent by: The Ashmolean Museum, Oxford; (Marshall Gift through the National Art Collections Fund, 1957).

Literature: illustrated in Marshall, op. cit., plate 7, no. 110.

93

94

95 Courtesy of the Ashmolean Museum, Oxford.

96. A Junket Dish,
with moulded wavy sides and a plain cartouche-shaped bottom, richly painted in the Kakiemon style with a pair of phoenix birds, flowering plants, and a banded wheat-sheaf. The *Phoenix* pattern.
c. 1765-70.
Diameter: 25.4 cm.   Mark: none.

There are two versions of this pattern found on Worcester porcelain, of which this is the more elaborate. They are both illustrated in Gerald Coke, op. cit., plates 25 (a) and (b), where the simpler version is attributed to Factory decoration and this version to the Giles workshop. However, in the catalogue of the Zorensky Collection it is suggested that 'the two are far too similar and it is likely both were decorated at the factory'. It might also be argued that the fact that there are two different versions makes it more likely that they came from two different sources, ie Factory and Giles, but the Giles attribution is clearly a matter of considerable doubt.
This pattern is not found on the porcelain of any other factory.
The quality of the painting and the gilding on pieces of this pattern is invariably of the highest standard and they must have been very costly to produce.

97. A Teapot,
of globular shape with moulded spout and plain loop handle, painted in sea-green monochrome and gilding with a flowering chrysanthemum branch and scattered flower sprays outlined in black.
c. 1765-70.
Height: 15.2 cm.   Mark: none.
Literature: illustrated in Robyn Robb, *2003 Exhibition,* catalogue, no. 16. A coffee pot of the same pattern is illustrated in the catalogue of Albert Amor's 1988 exhibition, *The Albrecht Collection, the Japanese Influence on 18th Century English Porcelain,* no.60.

Clearly the inspiration for this pattern was oriental decoration, but it does not appear to be a copy of any recorded original. Two versions of the pattern exist, this one and one in which a much paler green has been used: an example of the latter is a spoon tray illustrated in Spero and Sandon, op. cit. no.292, where the painting is considered to be Factory decoration. However, the use of gilding in conjunction with green monochrome, and the somewhat random way in which flower sprays have been painted round the spout suggest a Giles rather than a Factory origin, but, as with the other possible Giles oriental patterns, there is no consensus of expert opinion.

96

97

One of the features of his decoration for which James Giles is justly famous is his gilding, particularly the fine *ciselé* gilding usually found in conjunction with coloured grounds. It has been suggested by a number of authorities[1] that Giles's skill in this area arose from the training he would have received as a result of his apprenticeship to a jeweller, but this seems unlikely. In the first place we do not know whether Giles's master, John Arthur, was a maker of jewellery or a retailer of jewellery. Even if he was a maker, there is no reason to assume that applying gilding to porcelain would have been one of the skills that the young James Giles would have learnt. Indeed, there is some evidence to the contrary. If Giles had become expert in gilding porcelain during his apprenticeship, one would have expected him to have exploited this advantage as soon as he had established his own workshop, but this is not the case. As we have seen, in the early years of his enterprise, Giles was decorating mainly Chinese porcelain, and the gilding on the wares which are attributed to his workshop during this period is modest - simple dentil edges, birds-eye and sprig borders, and gilded bands round foot rims. Moreover, Giles had difficulty in making his gilding adhere to the hard paste Chinese porcelain, since much of it has been rubbed away.

The gilding on Giles's early Worcester porcelain is also unambitious, and in some cases poorly executed. It is not until the introduction of the ground colours of the middle to late 1760s that his fine *ciselé* gilding first appears, and the most plausible explanation for this is that the workshop had, for the first time, the staff with the necessary skills. This period coincided with the decline of the Chelsea Factory leading to its closure and take-over by William Duesbury in 1768. It is at least possible that the sudden appearance of superb gilding on Giles decorated wares was the result of the engagement of expert gilders from Chelsea.

The Giles workshop produced a number of services whose only decoration is gilding. Although these are not particularly sought after by present day collectors, they must have been highly valued by the contemporary market, judging by the quality of the porcelain that was chosen for some of these patterns. An example is the teapot, no. 98, - with its fluted form, entwined handle and moulded spout, this must have been one of the more costly teapot forms that Giles bought from the Factory. Although the gilding is sparse, the finished effect is certainly pleasing, and the fluting of the pot and cover are seen to best effect because of the absence of other decoration.

The teacup and saucer, no. 100, is an example of gilding used as the only form of decoration on an overall *bleu céleste* ground, a form of decoration used by both Giles and the Worcester Factory.

---

[1] For example Gerald Coke, *In Search of James Giles,* page 63.

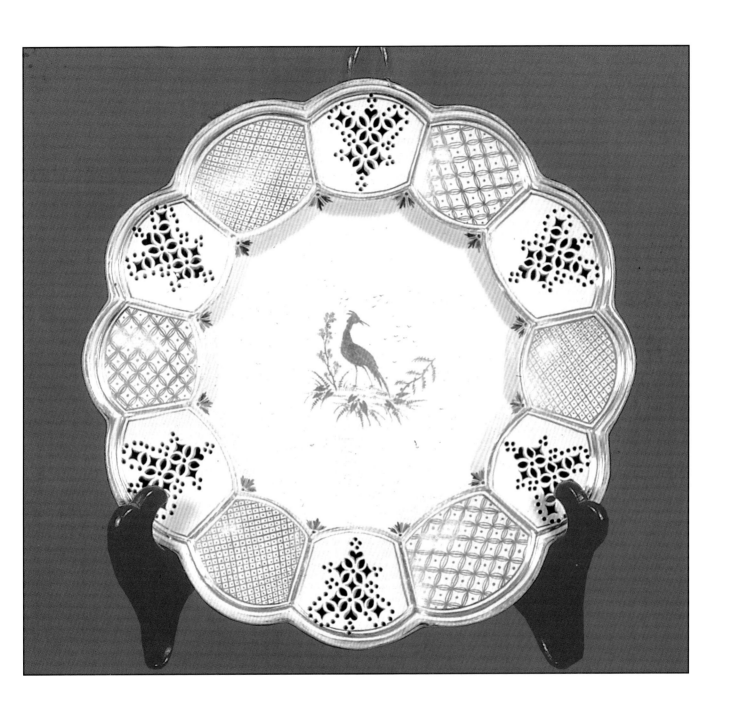

Creamware plate gilded in the workshop of James Giles, c.1775
Courtesy of Diana Edwards.

98. A Teapot and Cover,
of globular, fluted form, decorated with sparse gilding around the collar of the pot and on the spout, handle and cover.
c. 1768-73.
Height: 14.3 cm.   Mark: a fretted square in under-glaze blue.
Literature: Gerald Coke, op. cit., states (page 102) that 'most of the plain gilt decoration on white porcelain can be attributed to Giles, and fresh examples continue to appear, some of which may have been used only for one service'.

Giles features: dots of diminishing size on the handle and spout.

99. A Chocolate Cup and Stand,
decorated entirely in gilt with six true lovers' knots from which depend six festoons of flowers.
c.1768-73.
Diameter of stand: 15 cm.   Marks: none.

This is a common Giles pattern and a considerable number of services must have been decorated. A version with an unidentified crest added also exists. There was also a small bowl of Chinese porcelain with this pattern in the Watney Collection, lot 813 in Part III of the Phillips' sale on 1st November 2000. According to John Sandon (*The Dictionary of Worcester Porcelain,* page 113) these items were sold with or without covers. The 1774 sale contained a number of 'caudle cups', and this term may refer to these objects.
Giles features: gilding on the sides of the handles which also have chevrons and dots of diminishing size running down the backs, gilded band round the foot rim.

100. A Teacup and Saucer,
of solid turquoise ground with gilded rims and gilding on the handle.
c. 1770-75.
Diameter of saucer: 12.9 cm, height of cup: 4.9 cm.
Marks: crossed swords and *9* with dot in under-glaze blue.

All-over turquoise grounds were used by both Giles and the Worcester Factory, and they can only be distinguished by the associated gilding.
Lot 54 of the 1774 Christie's sale is described as 'a breakfast set 27 pieces blue celest and gold'.
Giles features: gilding on the sides of the handle, gilt dots of diminishing size down the back.

101. A Broth Bowl and Cover,
of fluted form with scroll handles, decorated with petal shaped panels in gilt.
The Gold Queen's pattern.
c.1770-75.
Height: 12 cm.   Mark: none.
Literature: an identical bowl, also without a stand, is illustrated in John Sandon, op.cit, page 85.

These covered bowls often have stands, but it is not clear whether this would originally have had one.
Lot 88 in the 1774 Christie's sale is described as 'six caudle cups and stands with white and gold wave' which could describe this object.
Giles features: gilt dots of diminishing size down backs of handles.

98   99

100   101

The painting of landscape scenes on porcelain was first carried out in Europe at the Meissen Factory in the early decades of the eighteenth century. The scenes were generally taken from prints and were often an amalgamation of different prints. By 1745 the Factory had over five thousand prints at its disposal. Meissen's lead was followed by other Continental factories, notably Vincennes/Sèvres and Tournai, and by the Chelsea Factory in England. All of these may have had an influence on Giles, but his inspiration appears to have come principally from Meissen and Chelsea.

It is clear from the number of different examples which have survived, including two of the four Grubbe plates, that services decorated with landscape scenes were an important part of Giles's output, and that those painted in green monochrome were his most favoured type of landscape decoration. The earliest examples are on Chinese porcelain, and date from the late 1750's, nos. 102-105, while lot 28 on the fifth day of Christie's 1774 sale is a tea service 'painted with different green landscapes', which suggests that the workshop was applying this type of decoration up until 1770 at least. No. 106 is an example of a 'mixed' service with a Chinese tea bowl and saucer and a Worcester coffee cup. It is rather coarsely painted with watery scenes including buildings with curious rounded tops and circular windows. The same distinctive features are found on the mug, no. 107, probably one of the earliest examples of Giles's green landscape decoration on Worcester porcelain. Later examples of green monochrome painting are the teacup and saucer, no. 110, almost certainly from the service most of which is at Saltram House in Devon, and the coffee pot, no. 111, which has the same distinctive gilt border as that on Grubbe plate 1.

Probably the best known of Giles's landscape services is painted in carmine monochrome. Grubbe plate 2 is an example, and about a dozen others are to be found in museums and private collections. A different technique is used in the actual painting. The green landscape services are outlined and highlighted in black and then washed over in green, while the painting on the carmine services is entirely in that colour. No. 109 is a plate from the Grubbe plate 2 service and no. 108 is one of a pair of heart-shaped dishes possibly made as additions to a Chelsea service. No. 113 is a teacup and saucer from the only tea service recorded with carmine landscape scenes; some other pieces are in the Royal Collection, and were exhibited in the 1951 Worcester Porcelain Bi-centenary Exhibition. Only two services painted with polychrome landscape scenes are recorded, and nos. 112 and 114 are examples from them.

In the past a number of pieces of Worcester porcelain painted in landscapes in iron red were also attributed to the Giles workshop, but most of these are now thought to be the work of other outside decorators. However, the Chinese coffee cup painted with a continuous watery scene in iron red, no. 105, has gilding strongly associated with the Giles workshop, and may well be a survivor from a Giles service with this rare decoration.

Many of the Giles landscape services feature ruins and buildings in classical style, a reflection of the interest in the classical world inspired by the Grand Tour and the excavations at Herculaneum and Pompeii, which were just beginning. As at Meissen, these scenes were almost certainly based on prints, and indeed the set from which the main architectural features used in the Grubbe plate 2 service were taken has recently been identified. The print from which the plate in the exhibition, no. 109, was taken, is illustrated in Fig. 5.

Fig. 4 Two 18th C source prints for painted landscapes on Giles porcelain and printed Worcester.

102. A Tea Bowl and Saucer,
of Chinese porcelain, painted with river scenes, outlined and highlighted in black and washed over in green monochrome.
c. 1758-63.
Diameter of saucer: 11.4 cm, height of bowl: 4 cm.   Marks: none.
Literature: a very similarly decorated Chinese coffee cup and saucer, possibly from the same service, were Lot 4 in Part 1 of Phillips' sale of the Watney Collection on 22nd September 1999, and are illustrated in the catalogue, where they are described as decorated 'probably in the Giles workshop'.

This style of painting has many features reminiscent of the work of Jefferyes Hamett O'Neale - the watery landscapes, the style of the buildings, the tree with horizontal branches, the distant poplars, the figures with small heads, and the flocks of high-flying birds are all characteristic of his work. The decoration on this service is, however, probably by another artist deliberately copying O'Neale's style.

103. A Coffee Cup,
of Chinese porcelain, painted with a continuous watery landscape scene, outlined in black and washed in green monochrome. Inside the rim there is an elaborate gilt tasselled, birds-eye border.
c.1758-63
Height: 6.4 cm.   Mark: none.
Provenance: the Watney Collection, and sold in Part II of the Phillips' sale on 10th May 2000, Lot 450.

Literature: this cup is illustrated by Dr Bernard Watney, *ECC Transactions,* Volume 14, Part 3, plate 2, together with a teapot from the same service in the Victoria & Albert Museum. In this paper Dr Watney argues that the unusual gilt border inside the rim of this cup is also found on a New Hall cup decorated and signed by Fidelle Duvivier, and that this cup may, therefore, have been decorated by Duvivier, working in the Giles workshop. The solid gilt handle and the broad gilt band, which were only used on the finest services, are strongly indicative of Giles decoration, and suggest that Duvivier may have used Giles's firing and gilding facilities, even if he was not actually employed by Giles.

104. A Saucer,
of Chinese porcelain, with a heavy gilt dentil rim, painted with a rustic scene outlined and highlighted in black and washed over in green monochrome.
c. 1758-63.
Diameter: 12.3 cm.   Mark: none.
Provenance: the Watney Collection and sold in Part II of the Phillips' sale on 10th May 2000, Lot 450.

In the catalogue of the Watney sale this decoration is described as 'associated with the Giles workshop'.

105. A Coffee Cup,
of Chinese porcelain, painted in iron red with a continuous watery landscape scene of buildings, trees, and figures including a man in a boat.
c.1758-63.
Height of cup: 6.4 cm.   Mark: none.

Giles features: gilt birds-eye and sprig border, gilt band round foot rim, and gilding on handle.

102   103

104   105

106. A Tea Bowl, a Coffee cup and a Saucer,
the tea bowl and saucer of Chinese porcelain, and the coffee cup of Worcester porcelain, all painted with watery landscape scenes with buildings and trees, outlined and highlighted in black and washed over in green monochrome.
c. 1760-65.
Diameter of saucer: 12.3 cm, height of coffee cup: 6.3cm, height of tea bowl: 4 cm.   Mark: none.
Provenance: the Watney Collection and sold in Part I of the Phillips sale on 22nd September 1999, Lot 196.

Rather crudely painted landscape scenes similar to those on these Chinese and Worcester tea wares, with watery foregrounds and tall buildings with distinctive rounded roofs and circular windows, are also found on Giles decorated Worcester mugs, no. 107.
Assuming that these three pieces were originally part of the same service, they constitute an example of one of Giles's so-called 'mixed' services, i.e. made up of both Chinese and Worcester porcelain.
Giles features: gilt birds-eye and sprig order, gilded bands round the foot rims of the cup and bowl, gilding on the cup handle.

107. A Mug,
painted opposite the handle, in a barbed panel edged with narrow black and iron red lines, is a watery landscape scene. To the right of the panel there is a bird perched on a leafy branch, and to the left there are three small birds in flight. The whole is painted in green monochrome, outlined and highlighted in black.
c. 1760-65.
Height: 19 cm.   Mark: none.
Provenance: the Watney Collection and sold in Part II of the Phillips' sale on 10th May 2000, Lot 589.

This unusual shape of panel with the black and iron red border is confined to mugs, straight-sided and bell-shaped, and painted either with landscape scenes and birds in green, as here, or with a 'Fancy Bird' and flowers, as in no. 56.
The distinctive, rather crudely painted landscape scenes on this mug are clearly by the same hand as those on the trio, no. 106.

108. A Dish,
of kidney shape, painted in carmine monochrome with figures beside a river and ruins, trees and a mountain in the background, all enclosed within a narrow scalloped border. The rim has a brown edge.
c. 1763-68.
Width: 25.7 cm.   Mark: none.
Literature: the companion dish, now in the Victoria & Albert Museum, is illustrated in Coke, op. cit., plate 12(b).

In the caption to his illustration, Coke describes the decoration as 'in the Chelsea style, which could be a replacement'. In the Victoria & Albert Museum there is a Chelsea plate painted by Jefferyes Hamett O'Neale in purple monochrome in a very similar style to these Worcester dishes, and another Chelsea plate from the same service was sold in the Phillips sale of 12th December 2001, Lot 70. The fact that there are two such clearly matching Worcester dishes suggests that they may have been decorated by Giles as later additions to the Chelsea service.

106

107   108

The Worcester dish now in the Victoria & Albert Museum was previously in the Parkinson Collection, and at the sale at Sotheby's in March 1966 it was catalogued as painted by O'Neale also. However, a close examination of the Worcester dishes against the Chelsea plate makes it clear that, although very similar, the decoration is by different hands.

109. A Plate,
painted with a landscape scene in carmine monochrome. Around the rim are five flower sprays, also in carmine.
c.1765-70.
Diameter: 22.4 cm.   Mark: none.
Lent by: The Ashmolean Museum, Oxford; (Marshall Gift through the National Art Collections Fund, 1957).
Literature: illustrated in Dinah Reynolds, *Worcester Porcelain in the Ashmolean Museum*, plate 30, page 69.

This plate has precisely the same style of carmine landscape scene and flower border as that on Grubbe Plate 2 in the Victoria & Albert Museum. About a dozen different plates from this service are known, and there are examples in the Museum of Worcester Porcelain, and the British Museum. The print from which the main architectural feature is copied is reproduced in Fig. 5 page 125.
Giles features: tulip with divergent petals, auriculas, convolvulus with trailing tendril.

110. A Teacup and Saucer,
painted with landscape scenes, outlined and highlighted in black and washed over in green monochrome.
c.1765-70.
Diameter of saucer: 13 cm, height of cup: 5 cm.
Marks: crossed swords and *9* with a dot in under-glaze blue.
Provenance: the Anthony Wood Collection.
Literature: illustrated in Robyn Robb, *2003 Exhibition Catalogue*, no.3.
Exhibited: Dreweatt Neate & Dyson Perrins Worcester Porcelain Exhibition, 1995.
        Albert Amor 2001 Exhibition, *Worcester Porcelain, 1751-2001.*

This teacup and saucer are almost certainly from the service at Saltram House in Devon, which is complete apart from four teacups and saucers.
The painting is probably by the same hand as the tea and coffee service at Corsham Court in Wiltshire, and the coffee pot, no. 111.
Giles features: gilt handle, gilt band round foot rim of cup.

111. A Coffee Pot,
of baluster shape painted with a continuous watery landscape, outlined and highlighted in black and washed over in green monochrome.
c.1765-70.
Height: 21.6 cm.   Mark: none.
Provenance: the Zorensky Collection, No. 446; and sold in Part II of the Bonhams sale on 23rd February 2005, Lot 227.
Literature: illustrated in Simon Spero and John Sandon, op. cit. No. 446.

109 Courtesy of the Ashmolean Museum, Oxford

110

111 Courtesy of Bonhams

A curious feature of this pot, and the similarly decorated one at Saltram House is that the knop on the cover is painted in polychrome enamels, while the knops on all other objects decorated with green landscapes are gilded.

Giles features: gilt Grubbe Plate I type border, gilt band round the foot rim, gilding on sides of the handle and chevrons down the back of the handle.

112. A Plate,

painted with a landscape scene in colours, within a border of two concentric blue lines.
c.1768-73.
Diameter: 22.8 cm.   Mark: none.

The distinctive border is copied from Sèvres, and is found on other Giles patterns - no. 13 and 23.
This is one of only two Giles landscape services painted in colours: an example from the other service is no. 114. Lot 46 of the first day of Christie's sale of Giles stock on 21st March 1774 is described as 'twelve plates painted with different landscapes in colour', and this could refer to either of these services.
Giles features: border of concentric, narrow blue bands with gilt bars.

113. A Teacup and Saucer,

painted in carmine with figures in a watery landscape scene.
c. 1765-70.
Diameter of saucer: 13.2 cm, height of cup: 5.1 cm.
Marks: crossed swords and *9* with a dot in under-glaze blue.
Lent by: The Ashmolean Museum, Oxford; (Marshall Gift through the National Art Collections Fund, 1957).
Literature: illustrated in Marshall, op. cit., plate 18, no. 333.

The decoration on this cup and saucer is very similar in style to that on Grubbe Plate 2, and the woman and child on the saucer are identical to those on Grubbe Plate 1, suggesting that they were taken from a common print source.
This cup and saucer are almost certainly from a single service. Two coffee cups and saucers, the sugar bowl and cover, and the milk jug and cover are in the Royal Collection, and the teapot stand was in the Albert Amor 1977 Exhibition, *James Giles, China and Enamel Painter*, no.1.
Giles features: gilt band round the foot rim of cup, gilding on the handle.

114. A Plate,

in the centre, surrounded by a black circle, is a landscape scene painted in colours. Around the rim are five purple floral sprays.
c. 1765-70.
Diameter: 22.6 cm.   Mark: none.
Lent by: The Ashmolean Museum, Oxford; (Marshall Gift through the National Art Collections Fund, 1957).
Literature: illustrated in Marshall, op. cit., plate 13, no. 235.

Two other plates from this service are in the Museum of Worcester Porcelain. See comment, no. 112.
Unlike most of Giles's landscape scenes which depict ruins and architectural features in classical style, the scenes on this service are probably copied from prints of Dutch or Flemish landscapes.
Giles features: winter jasmine.

113 Courtesy of the Ashmolean Museum, Oxford

112

114 Courtesy of the Ashmolean Museum, Oxford

The decoration on most of the pieces in this section has been attributed to the Giles workshop, but all have features which are uncharacteristic of the workshop's usual style, and which are discussed under each item.

Also included in this section is a tea bowl and saucer, no. 121, decorated with fancy birds, which some authorities have attributed to the hand of Duvivier père. The gilt dentil edge is similar to that found on other pieces of Chinese porcelain decorated in the Giles workshop, including a part tea service in the Victoria and Albert Museum painted with landscape scenes in green by Jefferyes Hamett O'Neale. There also exists a tea service of Chinese porcelain, painted by O'Neale with fables, and with a slightly crude version of the gilt border found on Grubbe Plate 1. These pieces again suggest that distinguished decorators like O'Neale and the Duviviers may have used Giles's gilding and firing facilities when they were not actually employed by a factory and were working freelance. The Chinese coffee cup painted with green landscapes, no. 103, which Dr Bernard Watney attributed to Fidelle Duvivier, is another example.

115. A Plate,
with scalloped edge and panels reserved against a scale blue ground. In the panels are transfer prints of ruins washed over in colours.
c. 1765-70.
Diameter: 19.6 cm.   Mark: a fretted square in under-glaze blue.

Both W B Honey and H R Marshall listed transfer-prints washed over in colours as attributable to the Giles workshop, but later authorities have considered them to have been Worcester Factory decoration. However, the gilding round the reserved panels on this plate is very similar to that around the panels on the Giles decorated spoon tray, no. 21. In addition the architectural features in the top panel are also found on the plate from the Grubbe Plate 2 landscape service, no. 109.

An identical plate is illustrated in Simon Spero and John Sandon, op. cit., no. 340, where the decoration is attributed to the Worcester Factory, although the authors do state that, '….it seems inconceivable that Worcester would have combined a black and white transfer print with a blue scale ground, a truly objectionable juxtaposition of colours'

Fig. 5   The 18th C source print for the scene in one of the reserves of the plate, no.115

116. A Spoon Tray,

of elongated hexagonal shape, painted with flowers and a moth.
c. 1765-70.
Length: 15 cm.   Mark: none.

The painting on this spoon tray does not look like Factory decoration, which suggests the work of an outside decorator. However, while the 'tulip with divergent petals' and the lilies are commonly used Giles flowers, these are different from his usual versions. Moreover, there is no evidence that the rim was ever gilded, which would be unusual for a Giles decorated object.

117. Plate,

Chelsea-Derby porcelain, painted in colours with three groups of fruit and insects.
c. 1770-75.
Diameter: 22.8 cm.   Mark: a gold anchor.
Literature: a Chelsea-Derby plate from the same service is illustrated in Coke, op. cit., plate 15 (b), together with a kidney-shaped dish of Worcester porcelain almost identically decorated.

Giles bought porcelain from Duesbury's Chelsea-Derby Factory, and the existence of pieces of Worcester porcelain of the same pattern and apparently painted by the same hand, makes a Giles attribution probable. However, much of the Chelsea-Derby bought by Giles was already decorated, and there are a number of non-Giles features about the decoration. Firstly, repeating patterns, while not unknown for Giles, are rare. The double gilt band round the rim is otherwise unknown on Giles pieces. The two butterflies are unlike other Giles butterflies, at any rate of this late date. The various fruits are similar to authentic Giles fruits, but not identical, while the palette used seems lighter than Giles's usual.

118. A Bowl,

Pennington's Liverpool porcelain, decorated with fruit and flowers in panels enclosed by a gilt border and reserved on an under-glaze wet blue ground, diapered with a star pattern in gilt.
c. 1770-75.
Diameter: 18.5 cm.   Mark: none.
Literature: a larger, but similarly decorated Pennington's bowl is illustrated in Coke, op. cit., plate 45 (b), where the painting is attributed to the Giles workshop and the same hand as that on the plate of the mixed Worcester and Chelsea-Derby service, no.117.

Dr Bernard Watney also attributed the decoration of these bowls to the Giles workshop in a paper entitled *James Giles and Liverpool Porcelain* published in *ECC Transactions*, vol. 14, part 3. In the same paper he illustrated a teapot, also of Pennington's Liverpool porcelain, decorated in precisely the same style as these bowls and almost certainly by the same hand. The teapot, no. 119, is identical in shape to the one illustrated by Watney, and again the flower painting is most probably by the same hand.

As in the case of the Chelsea-Derby plate, no. 117, the palette used appears to be paler than Giles's usual palette, and the gilding on the blue ground, both inside and outside the bowl, is unlike any Giles gilding.

119. A Teapot,

Pennington's Liverpool porcelain, decorated with flowers in panels enclosed within a gilt border and reserved on an under-glaze blue ground painted with gilt fronds. The handle and knop have been replaced.
c. 1770-75.

116

117

118

119

Height: 14 cm.   Mark: none.
Provenance: the Grant-Davidson Collection.

The pattern on this teapot appears to be otherwise unrecorded, but a Pennington's Liverpool teapot of identical shape, and decoration similar to that on the bowl, no.118, is illustrated by Dr Bernard Watney in *ECC Transactions,* vol. 14, part 3, *James Giles and Liverpool Porcelain.*   The flower painting on all three pieces is very similar and could well be by the same hand, but the palette is paler than Giles's usual palette, and the gilded fronds on the blue ground are unlike any other Giles gilding.

120. A Saucer Dish,
of fluted form, decorated with a cormorant standing on a turquoise rock with wings outstretched, holding a golden fish in its beak. On either side are rushes, flowers, leaves and rocks.
c. 1765.
Diameter: 17.5 cm.   Mark: a fretted square in under-glaze blue.
Literature: a slop basin and a coffee cup from the same service are illustrated in the catalogue of Albert Amor's 1994 Exhibition, *Treasures from Toronto II,* nos. 19 and 19a, where it is stated, 'The decoration represents some of the earlier work of the Giles atelier'.

The flower painting is similar to that found on a pair of mugs in the British Museum decorated with portraits of George III and Queen Charlotte, attributed to the Giles workshop.

121. A Tea Bowl and Saucer,
of Chinese porcelain, painted with fancy birds.
c. 1760.
Diameter of saucer: 12 cm, height of tea bowl: 4 cm.
Lent by E & H Manners.   Mark: none.

The bird painting has been attributed to the hand of Duvivier père on the grounds that the same hand is found on Chelsea and Tournai porcelain. The gilt dentil edge is a Giles feature. Compare with no. 102.

122. A Sugar Bowl,
of Chinese porcelain, painted with a chinoiserie landscape of buildings and figures, outlined in black and washed over in green monochrome.
c. 1757-62.
Diameter: 11.9 cm.
Provenance: Watney Collection

The chinoiserie design is possibly inspired by Pillement. Attributed to Giles by Dr Bernard Watney.

123. A Saucer
of Meissen porcelain, painted in colours with fancy birds on low bushes and standing on rocks surrounded by foliage. On the back the moulded grape vine is picked out in naturalistic colours.
Porcelain c. 1745, decoration c. 1764-68.
Diameter: 13.5cm.   Mark: crossed sword
Provenance: Watney Collection.

This is the only known Giles decoration on Continental porcelain. The enamels and style of painting are very similar to the mug, no. 52, and with the gilt dentil rim, should probably be firmly attributed to Giles.

120

121

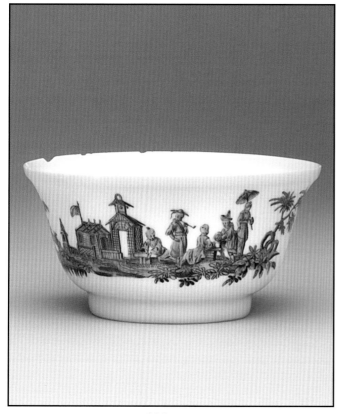

122

123

124   Floral decoration:
c.1765.

Guglet and basin	Gloucester City Museum
Ale glass	Museum of Worcester Porcelain
Goblet	Private Collection
Wineglass	Delomosne & Son Ltd
Beaker	Delomosne & Son Ltd
Worcester porcelain tea canister	Private Collection

The floral sprays on five of these items including the Worcester tea canister are by the same hand. The angular dentil border on the tea canister is frequently seen on glass. Note the classic divergent tulip on the tea canister and on the beaker. The guglet and basin is rare and illustrates the Grubbe border, as does the goblet.

125   Fruiting Vine:
c.1765

Burgundy decanter	Delomosne & Son Ltd
Architectural decanter	Gloucester City Museum
Goblet	Delomosne & Son Ltd

The subject on the Burgundy decanter is doubtless taken from a print – at present unidentified. It has been suggested it represents the King of Prussia with attendants. A trophy of arms on the reverse is an indication of military activity. The architectural subject relates to prints, illustrated here (Section X), which were clearly the source for some of the Giles subjects. Fruiting vine was commonly used in the 1760s.

Fig. 6   Scent flask, c.1765

124

125

126   Spiral Treatments
c.1765-70.
Green glass bowl and cover   Gloucester City Museum
Cordial decanter   Delomosne & Son Ltd

The covered bowl is an unusual piece. The small decanter is for cordial or liqueur. Its rococo trellis relates to that on the two pairs of vases, also of green glass, at the Corning Museum of Glass.

127   Neo-classical decoration on opaque-white glass:
c.1770-74.
Carafe   Museum of Worcester Porcelain
Decanter   Private Collection
Worcester cup and saucer   Museum of Worcester Porcelain

The carafe and decanter are closely related with their laurel trails and acanthus borders, while the so-called "bucrania" pattern appears both on opaque-white glass and Worcester porcelain as here. The pattern is described in the 1774 catalogue as "stags heads, pateras, festoons etc".

Fig. 7 Opaque glass beaker
Courtesy of Bristol Museum

126

127

128   Mosaic decoration
c.1775
Pair scent bottles in shagreen case   Museum of Worcester Porcelain
Oval bowl, cover and stand   Museum of Worcester Porcelain
Scent bottle of shuttle form   Museum of Worcester Porcelain
Pair cruet bottles   Gloucester City Museum

The term "Mosaic" appears in the 1774 catalogue. The oval bowl, cover and stand appear on the trade card of William Parker as well as on that of John Jacob, but, while Parker was one of the most prolific manufacturers of cut glass in London, Jacob was a retailer only.

129   Birds
c.1765-75
Decanter   Museum of Worcester Porcelain
Shuttle scent bottle of opaque-white glass   Museum of Worcester Porcelain
Dessert plate   Private Collection
Cream ware plate with pierced border   Muscum of Worcester Porcelain

The so-called "exotic" bird was much used by the atelier in the rococo period, presumably here drawn by the exponent of the flowers which form the secondary decoration. The cream ware plate is attributable on the grounds not only of the mosaic panels and striding bird but also of such detail as the heart-shaped leaves in the groundwork, seen again on the scent bottle.

Fig. 8 Detail of the Parker trade card, c1765
showing covered dish No 128.

128

129

Bibliography

Adams, Elizabeth, *Chelsea Porcelain*, 2001

Adams, Elizabeth & David Redstone, *Bow Porcelain*, 1981

American Ceramic Circle Bulletin/Number 2, Clarke, Samuel M, *Marks on Overglaze-decorated First-Period Worcester Porcelain*, 1973

Amor, Albert Limited, Exhibition Catalogues:-
> *The Drane Collection of Worcester Porcelain*, 1922
> *James Giles, China & Enamel Painter,1718-80*, 1977
> *The Golden Age, Masterpieces of 18th Century English Porcelain*, 1980
> *The Elegant Porcelain of James Giles*, 1983
> *A Celebration- 250 Years of Worcester Porcelain*, 2001

Barrett, Franklin A, *Worcester Porcelain & Lunds's Bristol*, 1966

Bonhams, Sale Catalogues,
> *The Zorensky Collection of Worcester Porcelain, Part I*, 16th March 2004
> *The Zorensky Collection of Worcester Porcelain, Part II*, 23rd February 2005

Clarke, Samuel M, *Worcester Porcelain in the Colonial Williamsburg Collection*, 1987

Coke, Gerald, *In Search of James Giles*, 1983

Dawson, Aileen, *French Porcelain, A Catalogue of the British Museum Collection*, 1994

Delomosne & Son Limited, *Gilding The Lily, Rare forms of decoration on English Glass of the later 18th century*, 1978

English Ceramic Circle Transactions:-
> Vol. 1, Part 3, Toppin, A J, *The china trade and some London chinamen*, 1935
> Vol. 1, Part 5, Honey, W B, *The work of James Giles*, 1937
> Vol. 2, Part 9, Marshall, H R, *Armorial Worcester of the first period*, 1946
> Vol. 3, Part 1, Marshall, H R, *James Giles, enameller*, 1952
> Vol. 3, Part 3, Tapp, W H, *James and John Giles and J. H. Neale*, 1955
> Vol. 6, Part 3, Charleston, R J, *A decorator of porcelain and glass - James Giles in a new light*, 1967
> Vol. 7, Part 1, Watney, Dr Bernard, *The King, the Nun and other figures*, 1968
> Vol. 10, Part 3, Clifford, T, *Some English ceramic vases and their sources. Part 1*, 1978
> Vol. 14, Part 3, Watney, Dr Bernard, *James Giles and Liverpool porcelain*, 1992
> Vol. 14, Part 3, Watney, Dr Bernard, *Four or five pointers that Fidelle Duvivier Worked for James Giles*, 1992
> Vol. 16, Part 3, Montagu, H, *The wrong James Giles?*, 1998

Godden, Geoffrey, *Eighteenth- Century English Porcelain*, 1985

Graham & Oxley (Antiques) Ltd, Exhibition Catalogue, *English Porcelain Painters of The 18th Century*, 1981

Hobson, R L, *Catalogue of the Frank Lloyd Collection of Worcester Porcelain*,1923

Mackenna, Dr F Severne, *Worcester Porcelain, The Wall Period and its Antecedents*, 1950

Mackenna, Dr F Severne, *The F S Mackenna Collection of English Porcelain, Part 2 Worcester*, 1973

Marshall, H R, *Coloured Worcester Porcelain of the First Period*, 1954

Phillips Son and Neale Limited, Sale Catalogues,
> *The Watney Collection, Part I*, 22nd September 1999
> *The Watney Collection, Part II*, 10th May 2000
> *The Watney Collection, Part III*, 1st November 2000

Reynolds, Dinah, *The Marshall collection of First Period Worcester Porcelain in the Ashmolean Museum, Oxford, 1988*.

Robb, Robyn, Exhibition Catalogue, *Fine 18th Century English Porcelain*, 2003

Sandon, Henry, *The Illustrated Guide to Worcester Porcelain 1751-93*, 1980

Sandon, John, *The Dictionary of Worcester Porcelain, Vol.1*, 1993

Spero, Simon, *Worcester Porcelain, The Klepser Collection*, 1984

Spero, Simon, *The Bowles Collection of 18th-Century English and French Porcelain*, 1995

Spero, Simon & John Sandon, *Worcester Porcelain, 1751-1790, The Zorensky Collection*, 1996

Young, Hilary, *English Porcelain, 1745-95, Its Makers, Design, Marketing and Consumption*, 1999

109a. A Plate,

painted with a landscape scene in carmine monochrome. Around the rim are flower sprays also in carmine.
c.1765-70.

Diameter: 22.4 cm.   Mark: none.

Provenance: the Zorensky Collection, No 425; and sold in Part II of the Bonhams sale on 23rd February 200
Lot 226.

See also no. 109, from the same service.
Giles features: convolvulus with trailing tendril and auriculas.

109a Photo courtesy of Bonhams